Table of Contents

Story Starters

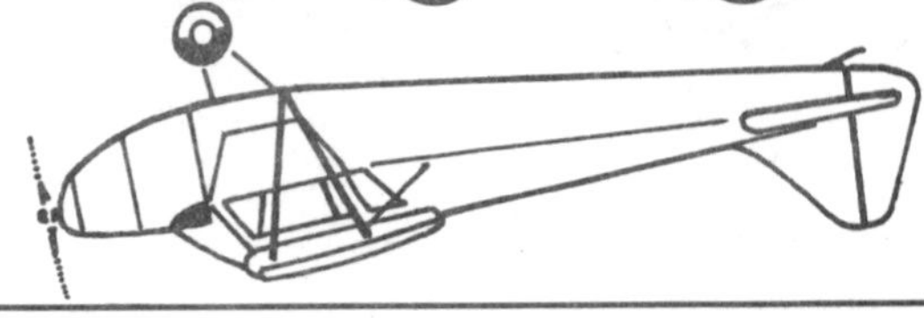

I was seated in the cockpit with the pilot when he/she . . .

Suddenly the hot air balloon . . .

There was something hovering in the sky like nothing I had ever seen before! . . .

Vocabulary

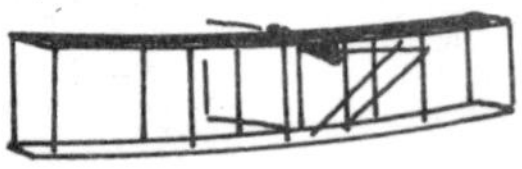

biplane
ascent
clouds
parachute
storm
air currents
gliding   soaring
engine
instrument panel
flight attendant
space shuttle

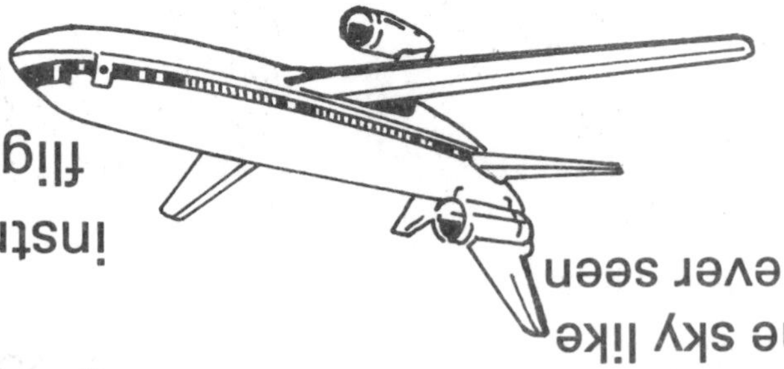

Facts and Fun

Make a time line of the history of aviation from the late 1700s until today.

Read about a famous aviator or astronaut. Then write a biography about that person.

Read about or visit an airport to find out what steps are necessary to keep an airplane in good working order. Write about this.

Air Transportation

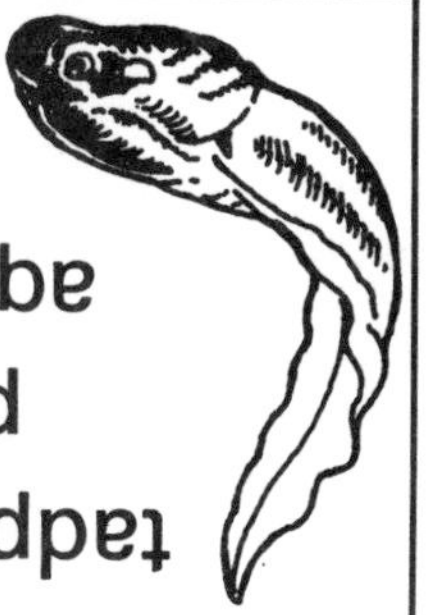

Vocabulary

vertebrates
gills lungs
coldblooded
camouflage
salamanders
frogs toads
tadpole polliwog
porous skin
aquatic leap
lunge

Story Starters

A witch turned me into a toad, and I went to school in my best friend's pocket. . . .

The gigantic salamander crawled into our town and . . .

I was about to jump into our pool when I noticed that it was full of tadpoles. . . .

Facts and Fun

Research the types of amphibians found in your area and make a field study guide for your school library.

Write two different definitions for the word *amphibian*. Draw a picture to go with each one.

Study different kinds of frogs. Make a chart comparing their characteristics.

Amphibians

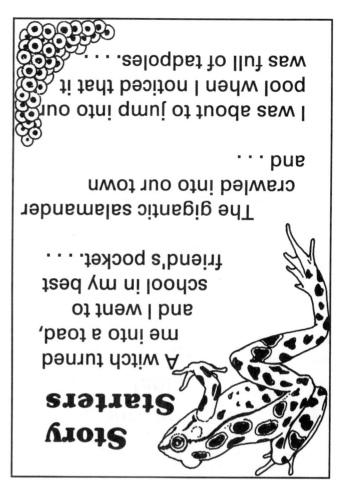

Amusement Park

Facts and Fun

Interview a few adults to find out how amusement parks have changed over the years. Write about the changes.

Design a new ride for an amusement park. Write about and illustrate it.

Tally your friends' favorite amusement park foods. Use this information to design a menu, using catchy names.

Story Starters

In the House of Mirrors, I saw a face staring back at me that was not my own. . . .

There was a most unusual prize awarded at the ringtoss game. . . .

We were stranded in the top car of the Ferris wheel . . .

Vocabulary

roller coaster
bumper cars
water rides
stuffed animals
candied apples
balloons
dizzy queasy
monorail
crowds
fun house
Ferris wheel
carousel
cotton candy
arcade games

Story Starters

Someone on a bicycle was headed right for me. I jumped out of the way. It was a chimpanzee! . . .

I looked out our back window and saw a gorilla delicately holding our kitten. . . .

The orangutan had escaped from the zoo. . . .

Vocabulary

chimpanzee
gibbon
orangutan
gorilla
baboon
forest
grassland
climber
hairy
intelligent

Facts and Fun

Design an ape playground. Remember to keep in mind all the things they like to do.

How will the destruction of forests affect apes? What can you do to help?

Research and report on Jane Goodall. Why were her findings important to the study of chimpanzees?

Apes

Armed Forces

Facts and Fun

Interview someone who served in one of the major wars. Use the information to write a news article.

Write a report about Arlington National Cemetery.

Select and write about a famous battle. Include details about who fought in it, where and when it took place, and so on.

Story Starters

I created a secret code to send messages out through enemy lines. . . .

Each button on my uniform has a special power. . . .

This maneuver was to be top secret! . . .

Vocabulary

military
platoon
basic training
warfare
artillery
MIA POW
reserves troops
commander officer
dog tag
advance retreat

Babysitting

Facts and Fun

Pretend you were teaching a class about babysitting. What would you include concerning emergencies, rules, and responsibilities?

Make a list of items you might include in a goodie bag to take along when babysitting. You might want to put one together yourself.

Make a poster advertising your qualifications as a babysitter.

Story Starters

This baby is the most difficult one I have ever watched! . . .

While reading a story to Nick, . . .

One night while babysitting, even I was afraid. . . .

Vocabulary

emergency
rules
bedtime
medicine
first aid
telephone
entertain
pajamas
television
responsibility
neighbor
diapers
refrigerator snacks

Back to School

Facts and Fun

Select three careers you think you might enjoy. Research to find out the educational requirements, qualifications, duties, and salary for each.

Interview school employees, such as the nurse, a cook, a teacher, and the custodian. Make a newsletter using the information you gather.

What things do you think should be taught in school that are not? Tell why.

Story Starters

You'll never believe what happened to my homework. . . .

I have several foolproof methods of passing notes in class without getting caught. . . .

A good teacher is one who . . .

Vocabulary

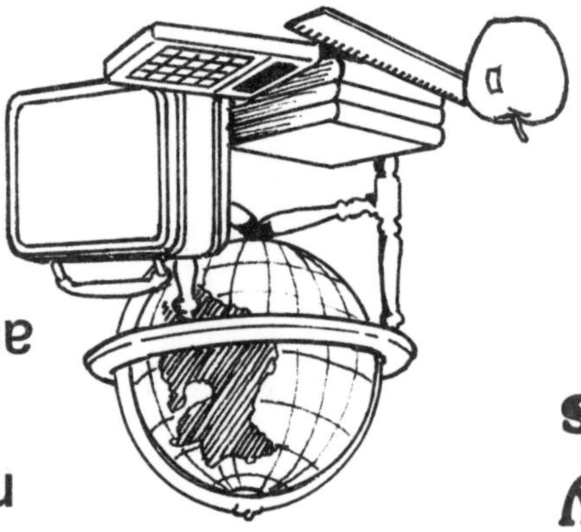

tests
research
tutor
assembly
homework
computers
study
principal
teacher pupil
classes
recite
gym
locker

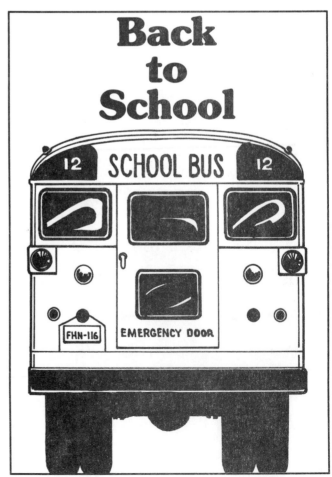

Ballet

Facts and Fun

Read the biography of a famous ballerina or danseur. Write about her or his life.

Watch a famous ballet such as *The Nutcracker.* Tell the story to your class.

Write a description of your or a friend's ballet lesson.

Story Starters

As the danseur lifted the ballerina over his head, he sneezed and . . .

While lifting my leg for an arabesque, my shoe flew into the audience. . . .

You wanted to take ballet lessons more than anything but your parents said they couldn't afford it. You just had to find a way. . . .

Vocabulary

barre

danseur ballerina

pointe

choreographer

pirouette

costume music scenery

tights leotard

practice

tutu

plié

positions

rehearsal performance

Basketball

Facts and Fun

Read about the history of basketball. Explain how the game has changed in the past 20 years.

Research a favorite professional player or team to write about it.

Interview your friends to find out their favorite teams. Make a chart showing each one's choice.

Vocabulary

fast break
goaltending
traveling turnover
technical foul
offensive foul
double dribble
man-to-man defense
hook shot hoop
zone defense
charging
slam-dunk

Story Starters

The Super Hoops were coming to town in two days. . . .

One fast break is all that I needed. . . .

If I could play basketball on any team, I would choose . . .

Bats

Facts and Fun

Make a set of cards with bat trivia questions. Challenge your friends to answer the questions.

Read about echolocation and compare this process to sonar and radar.

Think about Batman and Dracula. Then write about your own bat-related character and draw an illustration to show what he/she looks like.

Story Starters

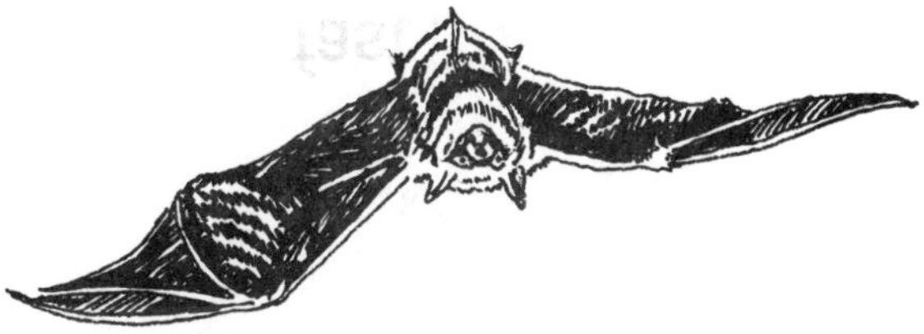

My pet, Billy Bat, helped protect me from the bully . . .

I was lost in the cave when suddenly I heard a squeaky voice. . . .

The bat awoke and . . .

Vocabulary

mammal
nocturnal
colony
navigate
echolocation
roost
insects
habitat
hibernate
migrate
predator
guano

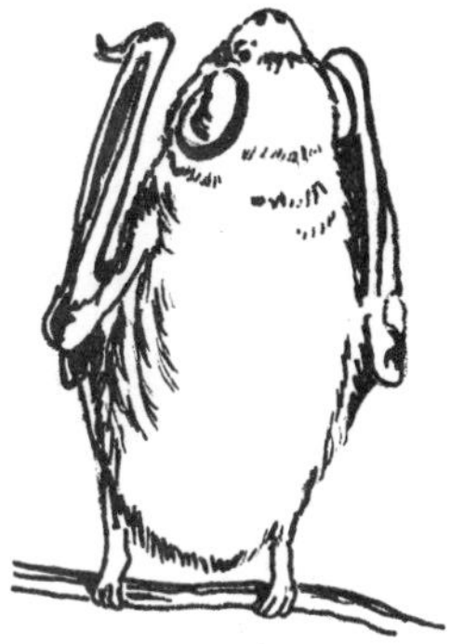

Story Starters

A giant bird grabbed our car and . . .

I unrolled the note from the carrier pigeon and read . . .

I got in big trouble when my parrot . . .

Vocabulary

molt
preen
migration
habitat territory
incubation
hatch
egg tooth
bill beak
talon
binoculars
ornithology
feathers
protective coloration

Facts and Fun

Read about ornithologists. Explain what they do.

Make a chart ordering 12 birds from smallest to largest.

Research to find out why Benjamin Franklin wanted to make the turkey our national bird. Would that have been a better choice than the eagle? Tell why or why not.

Birds

Bowling

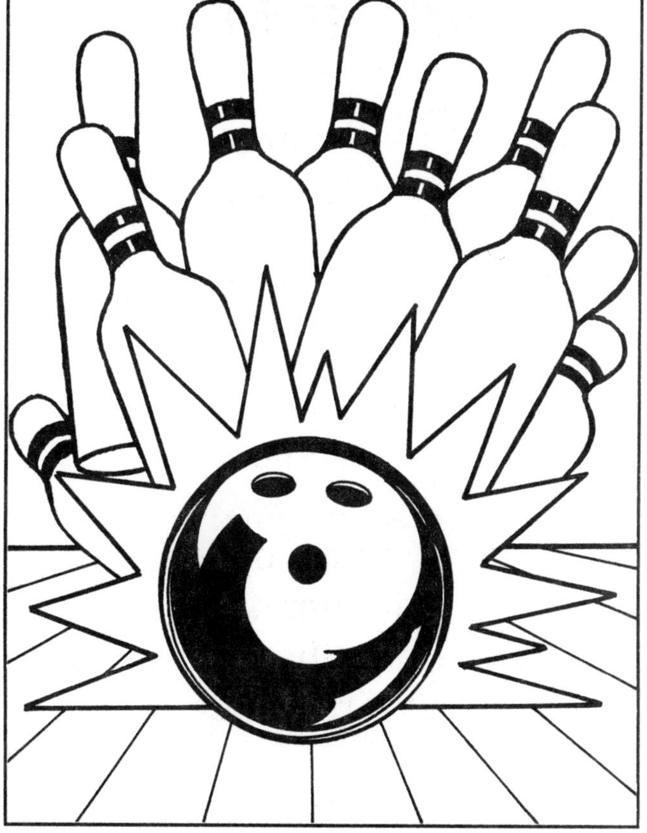

Facts and Fun

Read about a professional bowler and tell about his/her career.

Invent a new sport using pins and balls. Write the rules of this new game.

Read about sports in other countries that are similar to bowling. Write about them.

Story Starters

As I began to throw my ball, I realized that my thumb was stuck! . . .

Before my ball reached the pins, they quickly moved out of the way! . . .

Someone had greased the bottom of my bowling shoes. . . .

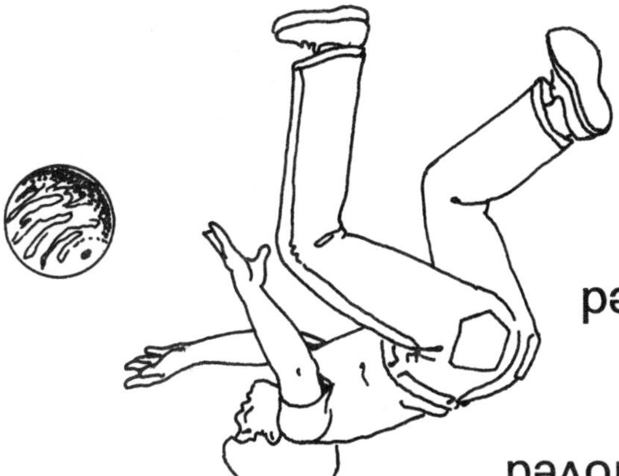

Vocabulary

strike spare
gutter ball
split
turkey
foul line
alley
curve
hook
pins
shoes
score
frame
tournament

Vocabulary

sportsmanship
pyramid spotter
megaphone
skit
spirit chant
pep rally
tryout
pompons
squad
competition
captain

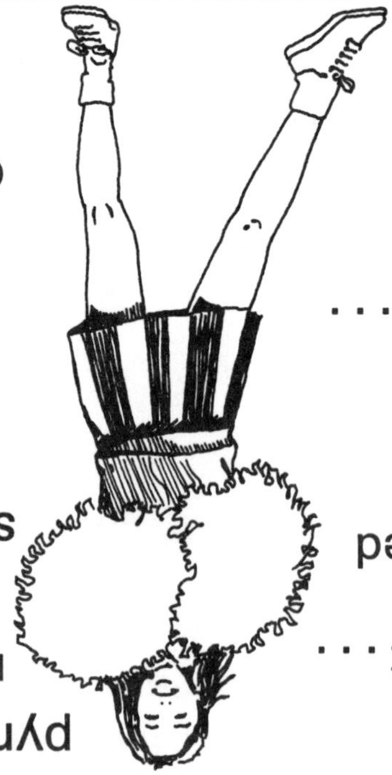

Story Starters

At the cheerleading tryout . . .

As the football team rushed onto the field . . .

When we finished, our pyramid was so high that . . .

Facts and Fun

Make a poster showing different gymnastics moves or jumps a cheerleader might use. Briefly describe each.

Design a cheerleading uniform for your favorite team.

Make up an original cheer for your school team or another favorite team.

Cheerleading

Civil War

Vocabulary

Union
Abraham Lincoln
Bull Run
Ulysses S. Grant
Fort Sumter
Confederacy
Robert E. Lee
Emancipation Proclamation
Appomattox Courthouse
slavery
Gettysburg
underground railroad
blue gray
Yankee rebel

Story Starters

The brothers fought on opposite sides. One for the North and one for the South. . . .

The slaves were carefully hidden in the wagon. . . .

When the first shot rang out . . .

Facts and Fun

Pretend you were responsible for a stop on the Underground Railroad. How would you hide the slaves and get them to their next stop?

Select one major battle of the war to investigate and explain in detail.

Draw a map showing the name and location of the major battles and who won each one.

Clouds

Facts and Fun

Find out which states have the most tornadoes. Why are they prone to have so many?

Design a poster explaining what you should do in the event of a thunderstorm.

Explain the different types of clouds and tell the weather associated with each.

Story Starters

As the cumulus clouds took shape, they seemed to come to life. . . .

Out of the thick fog came . . .

We could see the tornado rapidly approaching. . . .

Vocabulary

stratus
cumulus
water droplets
ice particles
cirrus
fog
water vapor
thunderstorm
condense
tornado
funnel

Communication

Facts and Fun

Prepare a time line that shows the history of communication.

Invent a new "secret code" and use it to write a message to a friend.

Choose one type of communication. Write about all of the jobs that are related to it.

Story Starters

From our ship we saw a message being flashed in Morse code. . . .

I was at a ballgame when suddenly my name was called over the public address system. . . .

The lighthouse keeper was sick. . . .

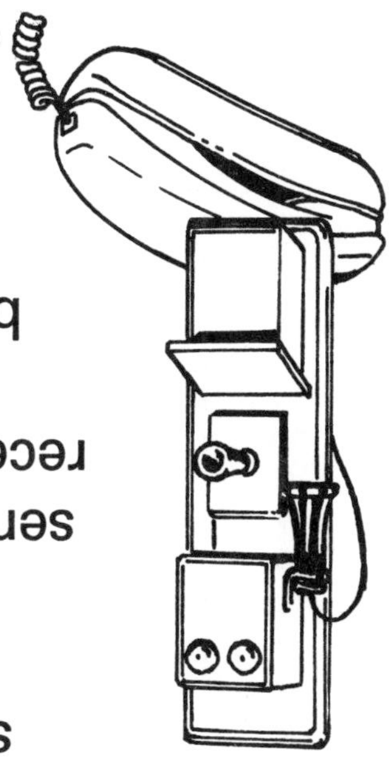

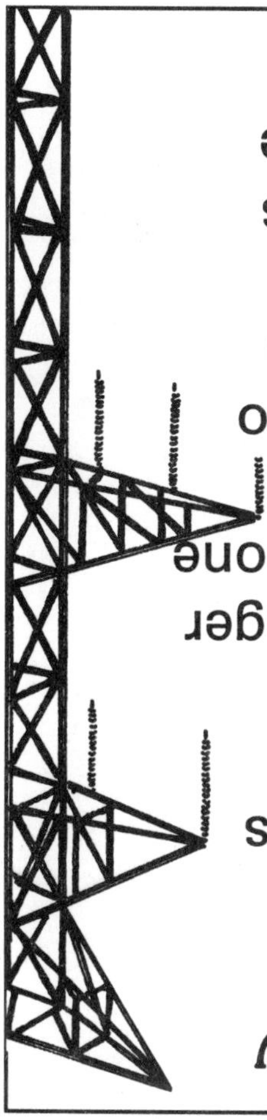

Vocabulary

television
Morse code
smoke signals
transmitting
semaphore
sender messenger
receiver telephone
telegraph
books radio
information
magazines
newspapers
walkie-talkie

Computer

Story Starters

When I turned on the computer, the face of a Pilgrim appeared on the screen. "Help me," she begged. . . .

One night when the school was closed, a computer hacker sneaked into the computer room and . . .

When I switched on the computer to finish my report, I was amazed to find it had been replaced with . . .

Vocabulary

joystick
monitor
space bar
printer
cursor
disk diskette
memory
menu
function key
enter
mouse
keyboard
terminal

Facts and Fun

Take a survey of 10 or more adults. Ask them if they use computers in their work. Write about the variety of ways computers are used.

Draw a diagram of a computer. Label the parts and write a basic set of instructions on how to use it.

Take a survey of your friends' favorite computer games. Graph the results.

Story Starters

The first permanent I ever gave . . .

One famous beautician in Hollywood had a very full day scheduled. . . .

When I took off the towel her hair came with it! Oops! . . .

Vocabulary

hairdresser   beautician
style
curl
straighten
appearance
appointment
salon
scalp
permanent
dye
curling iron
manicure
pedicure
blow dryer

Facts and Fun

Write about the many different things you can learn at a cosmetology school.

There is an opening at your shop for a beautician. Write a newspaper help wanted ad describing the position.

Cut out or draw pictures showing hairstyles from the past 100 years. Make a display, labeling the time period of each picture.

Cosmetologist

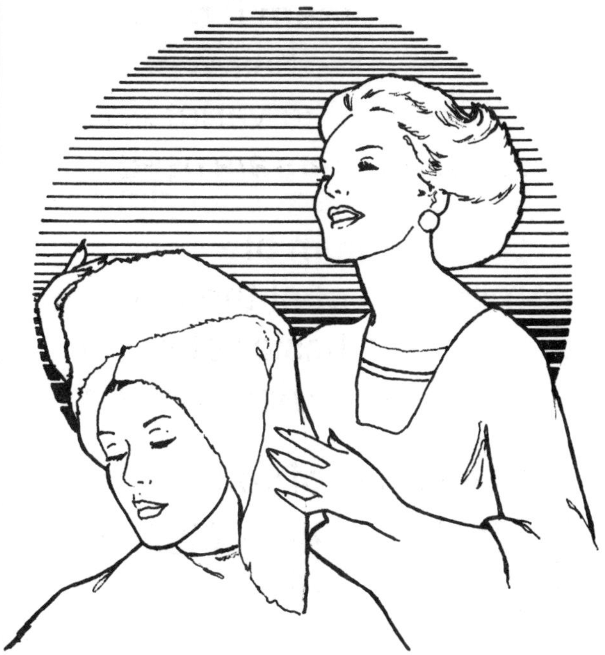

Vocabulary

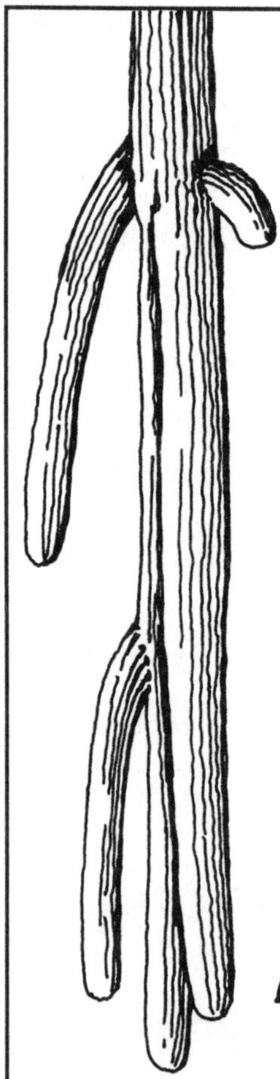

scorching
sandy
nomad
caravan
sand dune
cactus
lizard
dry
oasis
camel
thorns
mirage

Story Starters

We were lost in the desert. . . .

The camel race was the excitement for the day. . . .

The desert night was bitter cold. . . .

Facts and Fun

Tell about at least six animals that live in the desert and how they've adapted to their habitat.

Pretend you are spending a month alone in the desert and can bring only 15 things with you. What would you take?

Identify the location of several deserts by their longitude and latitude.

Deserts

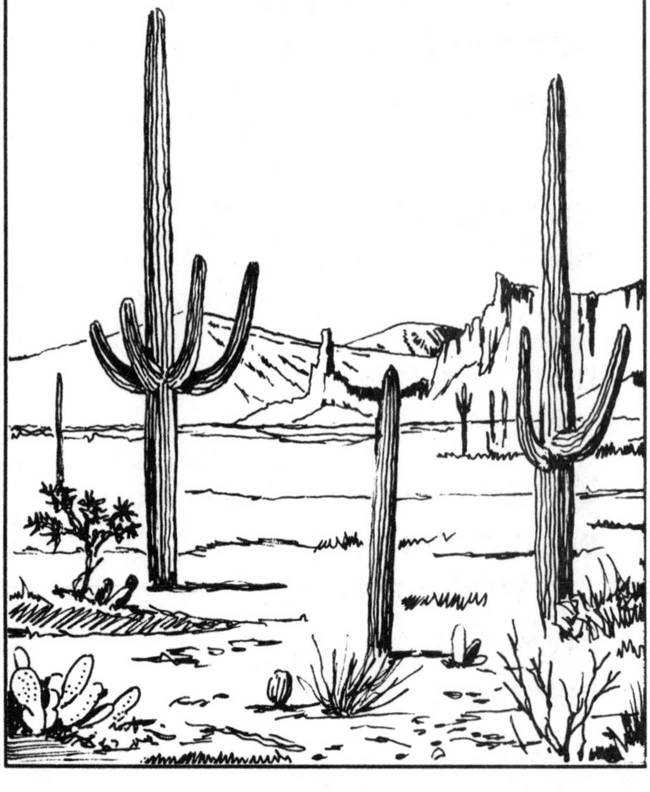

Story Starters

The dog team was harnessed to the sled and ready to go. . . .

I thought bringing my dog Tilly in for School Pet Day would be fun, however . . .

The hunt had begun. The dogs were off. . . .

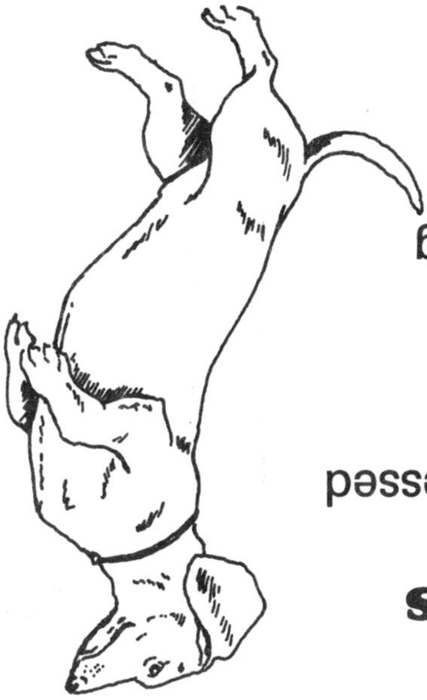

Vocabulary

domesticated
harness
groom
pedigree purebred
American Kennel Club
chew rawhide bone
ancestry
registered
mutt
hound
obedience school
companion
breed pointer terrier
sporting
herding

Facts and Fun

Write a commercial for a new dog food you have created.

Make a chart listing at least 15 breeds of dogs. Include when and where each breed was developed.

List the types of dogs that are helpful to man. Tell how each is helpful.

Write the name and breed of each dog that has lived in the White House and the President to which each belonged.

Dogs

Story Starters

As the dolphin glided past your boat, you noticed it was partially entangled in an old fishing net.

One night I accidentally became locked inside the dolphin arena at Sea World. . . .

During a storm, I was tossed from my boat into the sea. As I sank, I saw dark shapes swimming toward me. . . .

Vocabulary

aquatic
fluke
blowhole
mammal
dorsal fin
echolocation
trained
bottle-nosed
intelligent
marine
friendly playful
flipper

Facts and Fun

Make a book about the different types of dolphins. Make sure to include where they live and what they look like.

Find stories to read on how dolphins have helped man in dangerous situations.

Write from a dolphin's point of view about how it feels to live in an aquarium and be trained to do tricks.

Dolphins

Story Starters

The earthquake created a giant crack in the earth out of which crawled a . . .

The volcano began to grumble and rumble. . . .

The aftershock caused everyone to panic again. . . .

Vocabulary

volcano
erupt
avalanche
earthquake
epicenter
magma lava
crust mantle core
Richter scale
aftershock
fault plates
seismograph
disaster

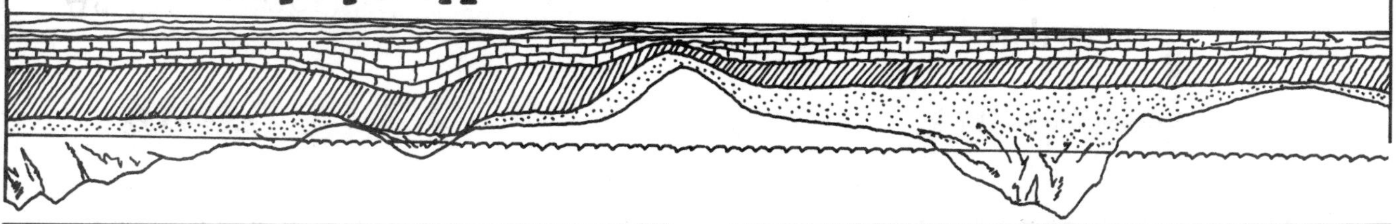

Facts and Fun

Read about a volcano that erupted within the last ten years. Tell how it affected the plant and animal population as well as the lives of the people living close to it.

Write about the work of a seismologist.

Find the fault lines in the United States and its bordering oceans. Draw and label them on a map.

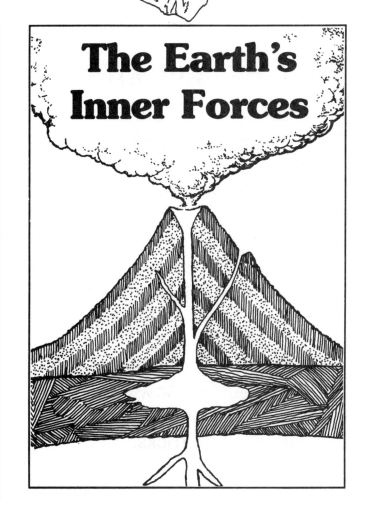

The Earth's Inner Forces

An Election

Story Starters

The presidential candidate is coming to our town tomorrow. I'm in charge of the parade! . . .

The election was in two days and both Alyson and Brian were sure they deserved to win. . . .

Boy, my life is sure different now that Mom is running for the office of U.S. President. . . .

Vocabulary

candidate
convention
nominate
amendment
primary
slogan
delegate
Democrat Republican
independent
democracy
polls ballot
campaign

Facts and Fun

You are running for class president. Write your campaign speech telling why you would be the best choice.

Research to find the campaign slogans of several past Presidents. Put them in a booklet.

Choose five other countries and tell how their leaders are chosen.

Vocabulary

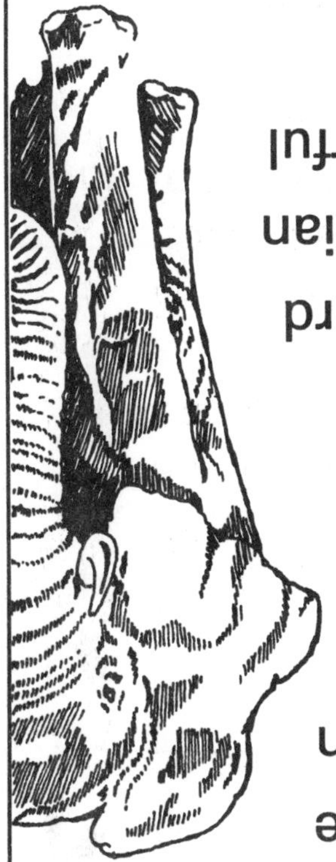

herbivore

pachyderm

tusks

ivory

trunk

hide

crashing herd

African Indian

powerful

Story Starters

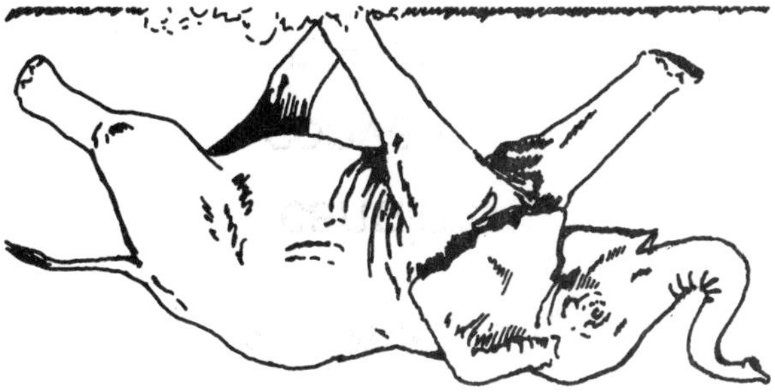

The enraged elephant rampaged through the . . .

The elephant was eating everything in sight . . .

The elephants saved the burning circus. . . .

Facts and Fun

Make up a fable on how the elephant came to have a trunk.

Study African and Indian elephants. Use a Venn diagram to compare them.

Write a comparison of mastodons, Woolly mammoths, and elephants. Illustrate your writing.

Look up the meaning of *howdah*. Explain how it relates to an elephant.

Elephants

Story Starters

I'm raising the last known pair of . . .

A thick-billed parrot swoops down into our backyard every night at midnight. . . .

The Florida panther pricked its ear at the strange sounds nearby. . . .

Vocabulary

Ocelot

American crocodile

Grizzly bear

California condor

Florida panther

Thick-billed parrot

Northern spotted owl

Steller's sea lion

Whooping crane

Bald eagle

Facts and Fun

Tell how littering, insecticides, and fires affect animals' habitats.

Write a letter to your representative in Congress asking for laws to be passed to protect animals.

Using resources at the library, make a list of other endangered animals. Write about what is being done to protect one of these animals.

Endangered Animals

Vocabulary

parent
extended family
grandparents
aunts uncles cousins
celebrations
rules
sibling brother sister
chores responsibility
reunions
traditions
sharing

Story Starters

When I woke up, I was shocked to discover I had become my mom. . . .

I was supposed to complete all my chores before Dad got home from work. He will be home in 15 minutes and I haven't started yet. . . .

This family reunion was certainly unusual. . . .

Facts and Fun

Make a list of your family rules. Then make up a list of rules you would have if you were a parent.

Think about a book you have read or a TV show or movie you have seen about a family that you really liked. Write a story based on that family.

Study the genealogy of your family. Make a family tree dating back as far as you can.

Family

Story Starters

Yikes! The cow is quacking, the horse is honking, and the sheep is oinking. . . .

The storm clouds were rolling in, and my brother and I had to get the cows in from the field. . . .

Boss Hog and the Piglet Patrol kept peace on the farm. . . .

Vocabulary

cattle
heifer calf
rooster hen chick
boar sow piglet
goat kid
mare stallion foal
bull cow
ewe lamb
sheep
duck duckling
gosling gander

Facts and Fun

Make a list of several farm animals and all the products that come from each one.

Read about the history of farming and then explain how raising farm animals today is different than it was in pioneer times.

Design a machine for tending chickens and collecting their eggs for shipping.

Farm Animals

Farming

Facts and Fun

Write a commercial for a new farm product. Design a logo and create a name for the product.

Write a newspaper article about a 4-H vegetable contest.

Use Popsicle sticks, construction paper, paper rolls, etc., to make a model of a modern-day farm.

Story Starters

It was time to harvest the corn, however, . . .

There is something strange growing in our fields instead of the corn we planted . . .

My vegetable stand attracted people from miles around. . . .

Vocabulary

tractor
combine
plow
grain elevator
till
harvest
fertilizer
cultivator
pesticide
picker
planter
irrigation
silo

Fire!

Facts and Fun

Compare a city-funded fire department with a community volunteer fire department.

Research and write about how firefighting has changed during the past 200 years.

Design a fire escape plan for your home.

Story Starters

The firefighter thought he saw someone in the upstairs window. . . .

My suspenders caught at the top of the pole as I started to slide down . . .

I could feel that the door of my upstairs bedroom was extremely hot. . . .

Vocabulary

alarm
flame retardant
pumpers
emergency
smoke flames sparks
ladder
controlled
siren
hydrants
combustion
fire extinguisher
smoke detectors
station
arson

Flavors

Facts and Fun

You are the owner of a new candy factory. Think up a clever name for your factory and the candies you will make.

Select eight flavors. Make lists of things that have each of these flavors.

Most ice cream and candy flavors are fruit. For what could you use vegetable or meat flavors?

Story Starters

The contest would decide the most creative new flavor combination. . . .

I bit into the juicy watermelon. It tasted like peanut butter! . . .

I saw a very odd fruit tree. I picked a fruit and cautiously took a bite. . . .

Vocabulary

cinnamon
peach
raspberry
bubble-gum
peppermint
peanut butter
licorice
vanilla
chocolate
strawberry
banana
blueberry
grape
cherry
lemon-lime
orange

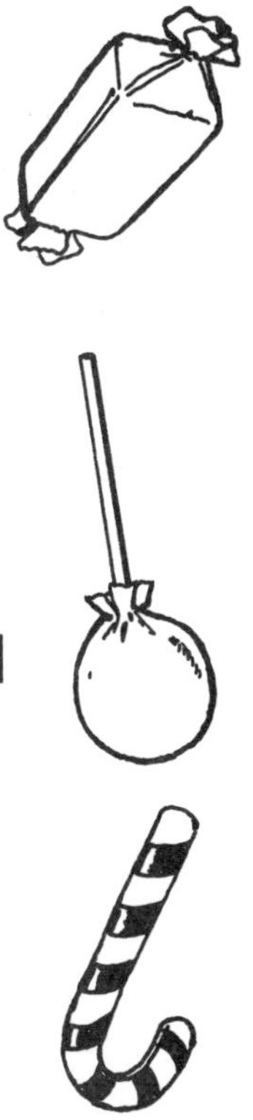

Story Starters

The football began calling out the plays. . . .

The Dallas Cowboys' coach called to see if I was interested in playing for them. . . .

I had just been put in the game to replace the injured star player when I saw the winning pass coming straight at me. . . .

Vocabulary

defense tackle
blitz sack
field goal official
professional end
flanker guard
touchdown
goal post
interception
fumble kickoff
quarterback
linebacker
helmet jersey
yard line
screen pass
shoulder pad

Facts and Fun

Select a football player or coach and write his biography.

Design a football card for your favorite player.

Write about the Heisman Memorial Trophy. Tell what it is and how it came about.

Football

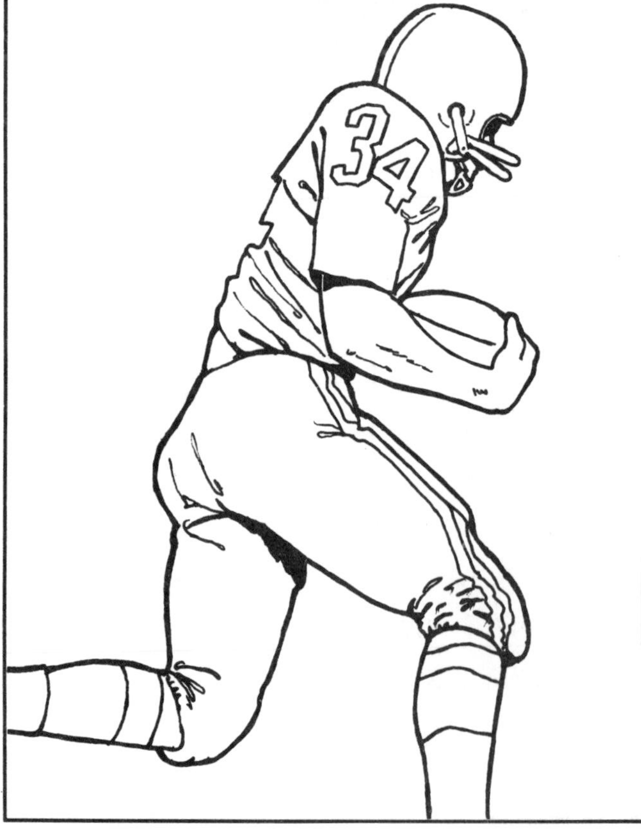

Story Starters

Robbie Roberts always talked in rhymes. He couldn't stop. . . .

Continue the alphabetic story: **A**nn **b**et **C**arl **d**idn't . . .

The field was alive with the sounds of nature. Bees buzzed, slithering snakes hissed, and . . .

Vocabulary

riddle
palindrome
joke
poem
limerick
secret code
alliteration
rhyme
onomatopoeia

Facts and Fun

Write a poem using alliteration.

Write a message using a secret code. Give it to someone in your class to decode.

Make up a palindrome.

Write a series of limericks about your family.

Fun with Words

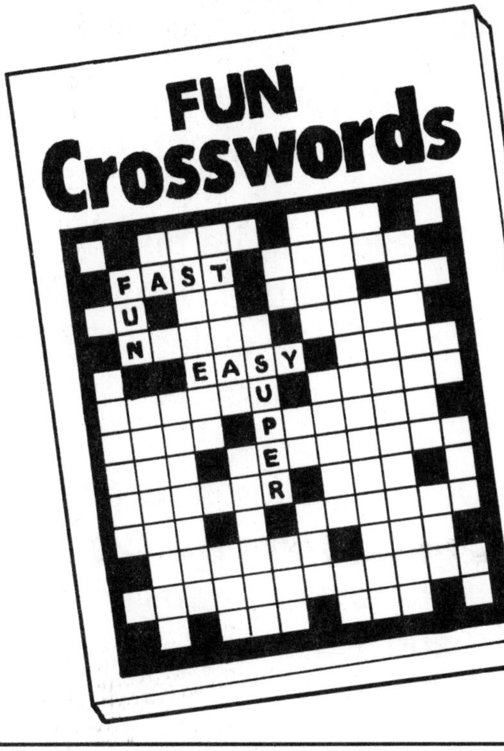

Golf

Facts and Fun

Read an article about a famous golfer. Summarize what you have read.

Research the history of the golf ball. What was it originally called? What was it made of?

Design a nine-hole golf course. Make sure you include sand traps and water hazards.

Story Starters

While on our way to the eighth green, the golf cart suddenly veered off in another direction as if it had a mind of its own. . . .

The crowd was silent as I putted my ball toward the hole. . . .

I took my stance in the sand trap. Immediately the sand gave way and I began to fall. . . .

Vocabulary

tee putter
slice hook
bogey
birdie eagle
cart drive
stroke
fairway
woods
green
clubs
sand trap
chip
hole irons

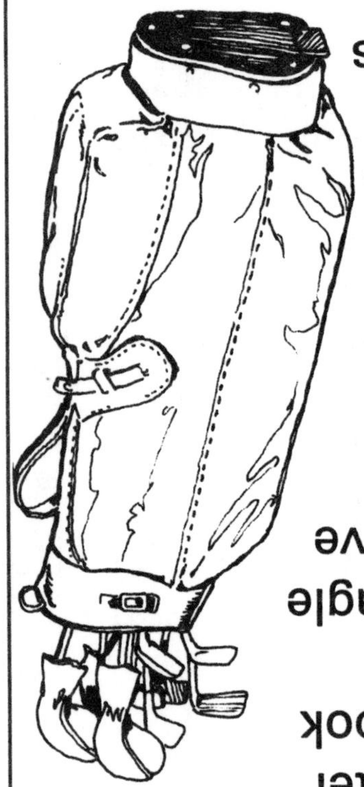

Gymnastics

Facts and Fun

Choose one type of gymnastic equipment. Using a stick person, draw a routine that could be done on it.

Research which team won the most gymnastics events in the latest Olympic Games. Which team won the second most? How many events did they win?

Make a book for beginning gymnasts that includes different gymnastic equipment, giving the name, a description, and a drawing of each.

Story Starters

As soon as I jumped onto the springboard . . .

My Olympic dream began when I first walked into the gymnastic center. . . .

The music for my routine was on the wrong speed. . . .

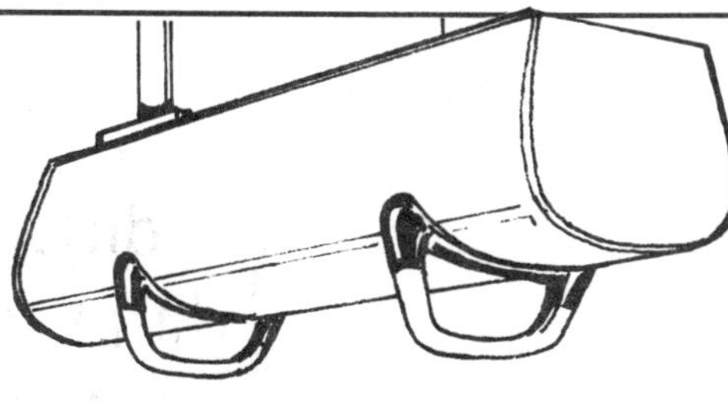

Vocabulary

routine
mat
rings
cartwheel
somersault
springboard
floor exercise
uneven bars
balance beam
parallel bars   vault
dismount
pommel horse
horizontal bar

Hawaii

Facts and Fun

Compare Hawaii to the mainland. How are they the same? Different?

Explain how a volcano is formed. Then make a model.

What happened in Pearl Harbor on December 7, 1941? Who does the U.S.S. *Arizona* Memorial honor?

Name the Hawaiian Islands in order of size beginning with the largest. Find out each island's nickname.

Story Starters

I was climbing a volcano when it suddenly began to shake! . . .

We were shipwrecked on Kahoolawe. . . .

The old man's mind drifted back to December 7, 1941, . . .

Vocabulary

erupt
aloha
flowers leis
hula
islands luau
ocean
volcano lava
pineapple
grass skirt
muumuu
sugar cane

Vocabulary

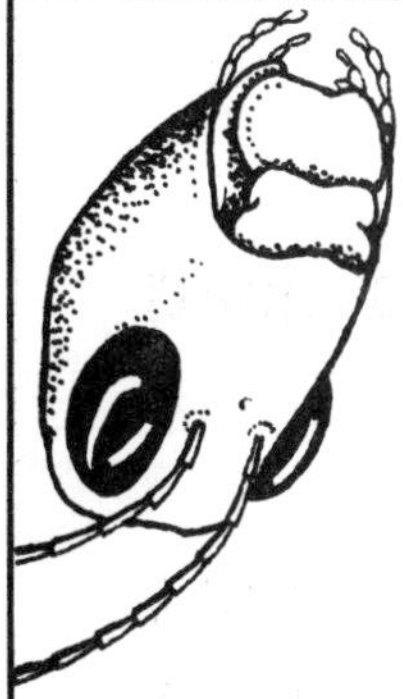

abdomen
antenna
compound eye
entomologist
pupa adult
colony
migrate
hibernate
larva egg
mandible
metamorphosis
molt
thorax head

Story Starters

I was kidnapped by a large ant colony. . . .

The butterfly frantically flew around my head, as if it were trying to tell me something. . . .

As I was doing lab experiments, a new insect emerged from . . .

Facts and Fun

Pick an insect to study. Write about and illustrate the stages of the insect's life. Describe how and why the insect is helpful or harmful to man and/or other animals.

Create a new insect. Describe the way it looks in each of its stages. Include its eating and living habits.

Take pictures of or draw several insects in their habitats. Label and describe each one.

Insects

Karate

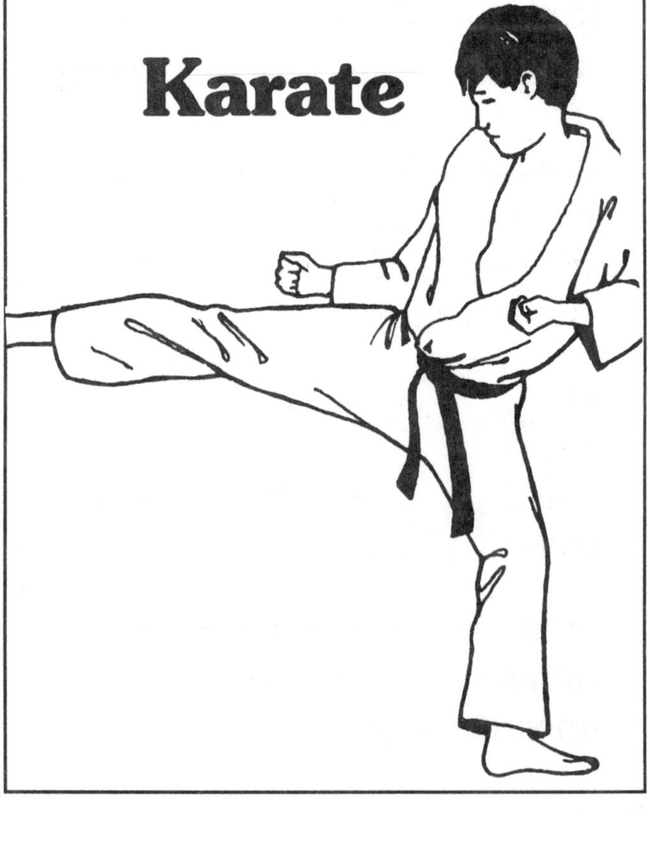

Facts and Fun

Explain how free-fighting competition is different from form competition.

Research the history of karate. Write a brief report.

Draw a white, a green, and a black karate belt. Describe what a person has to do to earn each one.

Story Starters

As my opponent raised his leg for the kick, I saw he had brass knuckles on his toes! . . .

I almost lost my nerve when I saw the size of my opponent. . . .

I knew I'd have to break six boards. . . .

Vocabulary

self-defense
kicks
martial arts
stances
rising block
combination
kata ri gi
counterattack
forms
bushido
belt
form competition
freefighting

Story Starters

The Duffy Award was no longer a dream. . . .

I needed to earn enough money to buy a kart. . . .

Everyone calls me Go-Kart Kelly because . . .

Vocabulary

sprint race
heats pit
competition
safety inspection
chasis engine
Duffy Award
speedway race
aerodynamic
enduro race
front fairing
road race

Facts and Fun

Find out how to become a member of the PKA (Professional Kart Association).

Find the names of the national champions of the last 5 years and choose one to write about.

Find out the differences between sprint, road, and speedway racing.

Karts

Vocabulary

Labor Day
Independence Day
New Year's Day
Veterans Day
Earth Day
Father's Day
Memorial Day
Presidents' Day
Martin Luther King Day
Columbus Day
Thanksgiving
Mother's Day
Flag Day
Groundhog Day

Story Starters

The turkey was missing. We had looked everywhere. The guests would be arriving soon. . . .

The brilliant fireworks lit the night sky . . .

Earth Day is a great day to . . .

My favorite holiday has always been . . .

Facts and Fun

Pretend you own a business. Write a speech that you would give to your employees on Labor Day.

Compile a booklet giving the origins of at least 10 American holidays.

Write a slogan for five holidays. For example, one for the Fourth of July might be "The land of the free is where I want to be."

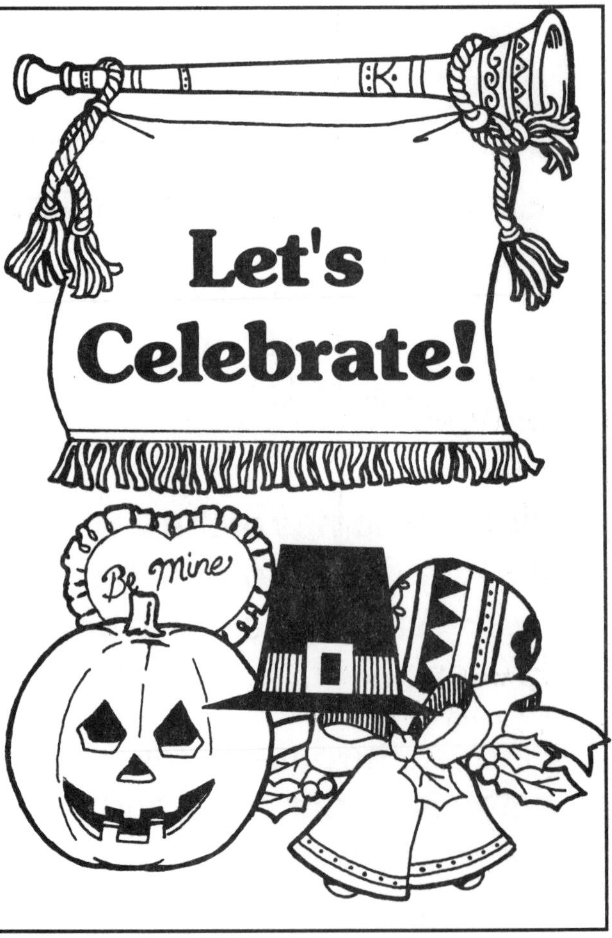

Vocabulary

illusionist
boxes
balls
escape artist
abracadabra
sleight of hand
top hat
cards
assistant
handcuffs
mentalist

Story Starters

I made my little brother magically disappear. Now I can't get him back. . . .

I performed my favorite magic trick at the school talent show. . . .

I intended to pull a rabbit out of my hat, but . . .

Facts and Fun

Give a report comparing two famous magicians.

Explain the differences between the five kinds of magic . . . sleight of hand, close-up, illusions, escape, and mentalist.

Present a magic trick to your class.

Magician

Story Starters

As she drove down the expressway, pieces of her car began flying off. She had just been to the mechanic. . . .

My car would only drive in reverse. . . .

I invented a new car alarm that . . .

Vocabulary

transmission
oil filter
alignment
antifreeze
brakes
maintenance
warranty
mileage
plugs points
transmission
carburetor
oil change
engine

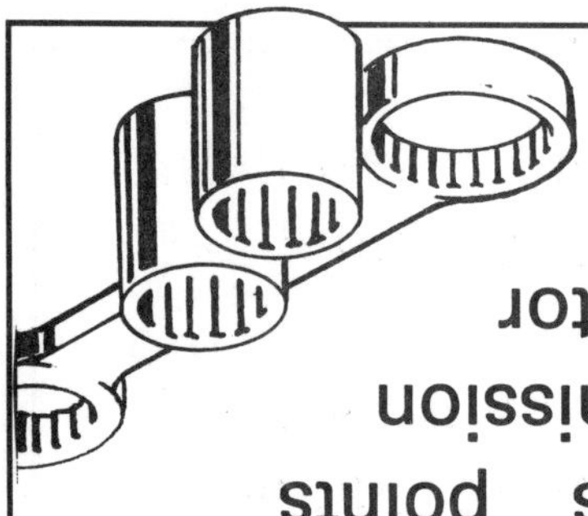

Facts and Fun

List some professions that rely on the knowledge of a good mechanic.

Research and write about future means of transportation. Tell what mechanical skills would be needed to care for these vehicles.

Draw an automobile engine and label its main parts. Explain what some of the parts do.

A Mechanic

Middle Ages

Facts and Fun

What three groups made up the feudal system? Tell what life was like for each of these groups.

Use paper rolls, cardboard, glue and construction paper to make a castle.

Create a coat of arms for your family and explain what it means.

Story Starters

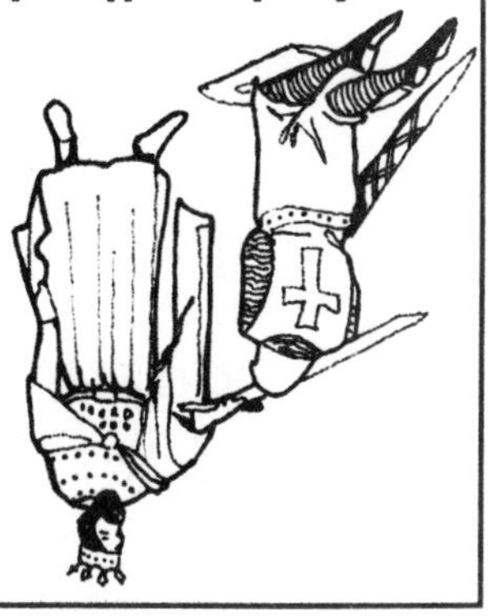

As I walked past the suit of armor, it began to follow me. . . .

I am a court jester and I have to entertain the King and his guests tonight. . . .

We planned to attack the neighboring castle. . . .

Vocabulary

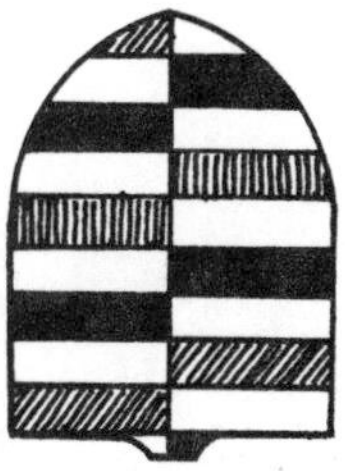

castle
knight
lord   lady
church
spear   shield
armor
feudalism
chivalry
joust
tournament
peasant
manor
Crusades
court jester

Story Starters

We had a contest to see who could think up the most ways to help clean up the earth. . . .

After I cleaned my closet, I found that I could recycle . . .

One day I decided that I was sick of the trash in the stream near my house so I . . .

Vocabulary

garbage trash
earth soil
recycle reduce reuse
conserving
toxic hazardous
landfill
litter
rain forest
air water
pollution
waste
wildlife
plants

Facts and Fun

Explain the history of Earth Day.

Write what you think the earth will be like 50 years from now.

What is the "Greenhouse Effect"?

Invent a new biodegradable product. Draw and write an advertisement for it.

Mother Earth

Vocabulary

Zeus
Athena
Minotaur
Aphrodite
Apollo
Pele
Ulysses
Cupid Mars
giant
cyclops centaurs
Pegasus
Satyr
Sirens
Olympus
Trojan War

Story Starters

I went into the barn to saddle my horse. He had sprouted wings. . . .

The fire goddess Pele was angry. . . .

Cupid threw his arrow at Mars and . . .

Facts and Fun

Create your own myth. Be sure to include the names and descriptions of your characters.

Research and then write about the Trojan War.

Create a mythical figure that is half man, half animal. Illustrate this figure and give its name, habitat, and other details.

Mythology

Oceans

Facts and Fun

Research and write about the tools oceanographers use to explore the ocean.

Write about several living things found in the ocean.

Describe the damage an oil spill can cause. What methods are used to clean up oil spills?

Compare the three main oceans. Name the countries that each one borders.

Story Starters

The whale was stranded. The boy had to get him back in the water. . . .

I went scuba diving. The undersea world was amazing. . . .

I have a pet sea horse that I ride under the ocean. . . .

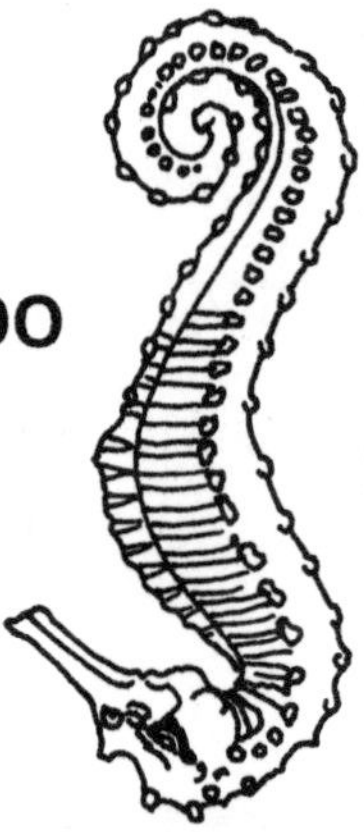

Vocabulary

tides
currents
oceanographers
waves
submersible
plankton
nekton
benthos
tsunami
kelp
sea floor
reef

Vocabulary

piano harp
performance rehearsal
musician conductor
piccolo flute
cymbals drums
clarinet
xylophone
bass violin
trumpet
French horn
saxophone
bassoon oboe
trombone
cello
viola

Story Starters

While conducting the orchestra, my baton became a magic wand. . . .

Oh, no! I practiced the wrong music for the big audition! . . .

A fiddler crab lived in my fiddle. . . .

Suddenly, in the middle of our performance . . .

Facts and Fun

Write about the instruments in the brass, woodwind, or string section.

If you could learn to play an instrument, which would you choose? Why? If you already play an instrument, tell why you chose it.

Study a famous composer and write about his/her life. Listen to Prokofiev's *Peter and the Wolf*. What instruments portray each character?

An Orchestra

Vocabulary

flags banners
horse patrol
floats
spectators
announcer
marching band
police car
convertible
grand marshal
parade route
uniforms costumes
judges' stand
king queen
baton twirlers
fire trucks

Story Starters

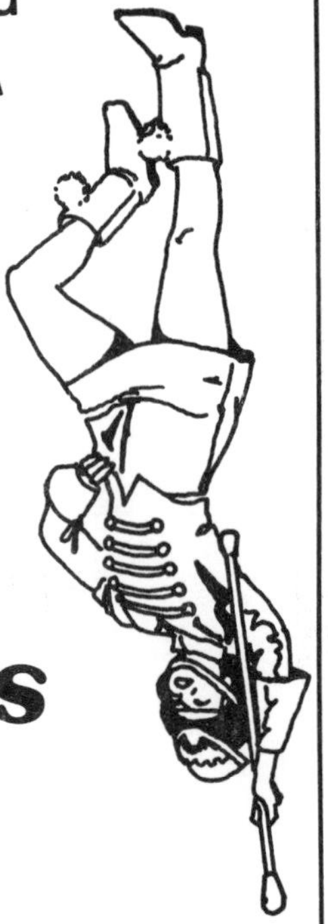

Just as the Fourth of July parade began, . . .

I was the guest of honor in a Welcome Home parade. . . .

The tiger got loose during the circus parade. . . .

Facts and Fun

Write a newspaper ad that will convince people to come to a parade.

Study a street map of your town. Lay out a parade route. Write a set of directions from the beginning to the end of the route.

Design a float for the Rose Bowl parade. Label all the flowers you would use.

Parades

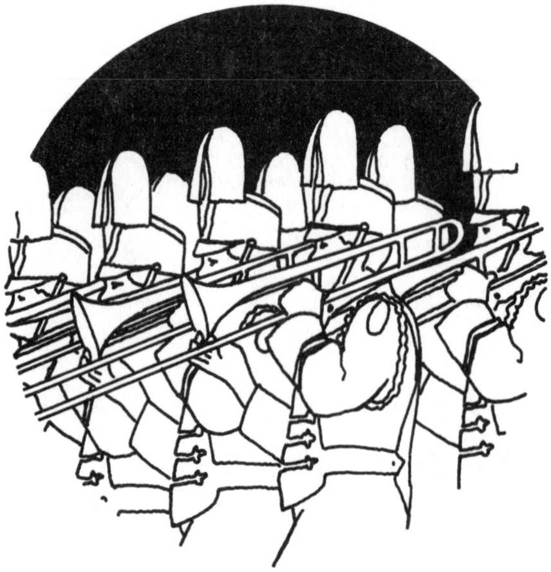

Story Starters

My assignment was to photograph the wildlife along the Amazon. . . .

The mystery was solved when I developed the film. . . .

She found a bottle on the beach. Inside was a roll of film. . . .

Vocabulary

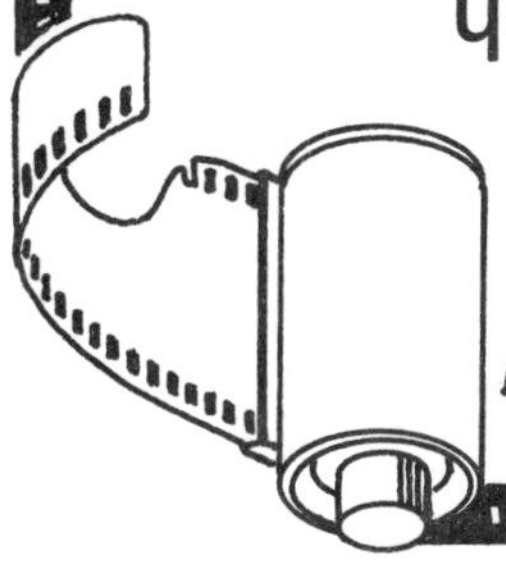

camera
shutter
tripod flash
develop
emulsion
viewfinder
telephoto lens
negative
exposure
light focus
aperture
wide-angle lens
photographer
composition

Photography

Facts and Fun

"A picture is worth a thousand words." Select a picture and write about what you see.

Collect several pictures of yourself. Place them on a time line and write a date and a caption for each.

Explain how the first cameras worked.

Facts and Fun

Create and name a new state. Make up a state flower, bird, song, and motto. Tell what products are produced or grown there.

Read about your state. Make a pamphlet advertising its tourist attractions.

Choose a state and design a new state flag for it. Explain what each part of the design stands for.

Pick Any State

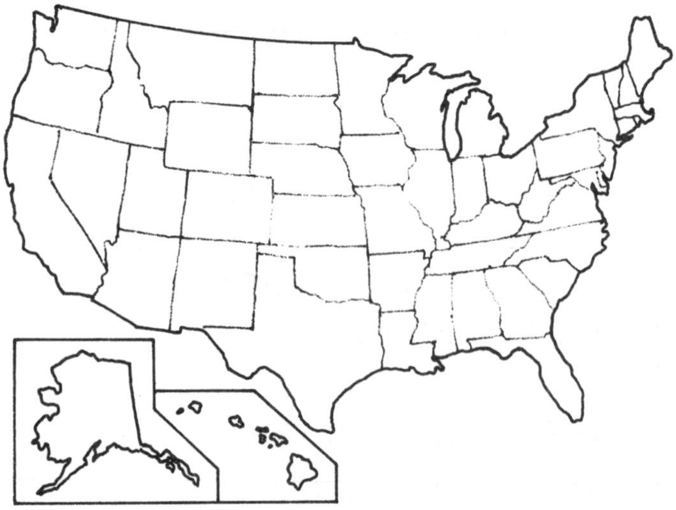

Story Starters

I was the cat in the governor's mansion. . . .

While riding my bike across the United States, I saw some beautiful sights. . . .

There were strange lights moving about at night in our state's historic village. . . .

Vocabulary

nickname
landforms
motto
recreation
historic events
agriculture
tree bird
climate flower
admission to Union
manufacturing
natural resources
capital

Pioneer

Facts and Fun

Read about pioneer life. Write a comparison of what pioneer youngsters did for fun compared with what you do for fun.

Make a model of a pioneer village using a large box lid, Popsicle sticks, sticks, and other materials.

Draw a map of the Natchez Trace, Santa Fe Trail, and Oregon Trail to show the westward movement.

Story Starters

My parents said I couldn't take my dog on the wagon train west. . . .

I became lost when our wagon stopped for the night. . . .

She dropped her lantern when she saw . . .

Vocabulary

frontier frontiersman
settler settlement
covered wagon
fort trading post
wilderness
westward trail
danger supplies
farmer hunter
log cabin sod hut
claim
house-raising
flatboat
trapper

Pirates

Facts and Fun

Read about Sir Henry Morgan, Blackbeard, and Captain Kidd. Write about what made each one notorious.

Design your own pirate flag and tell what the symbols represent.

Design and draw an outfit that only a pirate could love.

Story Starters

I was Blackbeard's parrot. . . .

We followed the map we had found in a bottle . . .

I looked in the spyglass and couldn't believe my eyes! . . .

Vocabulary

captain crew
buccaneer
rob raid
treasure chest
skull and crossbones
gangplank
booty
Jolly Roger
parrot
compass
spyglass
piracy

Planets

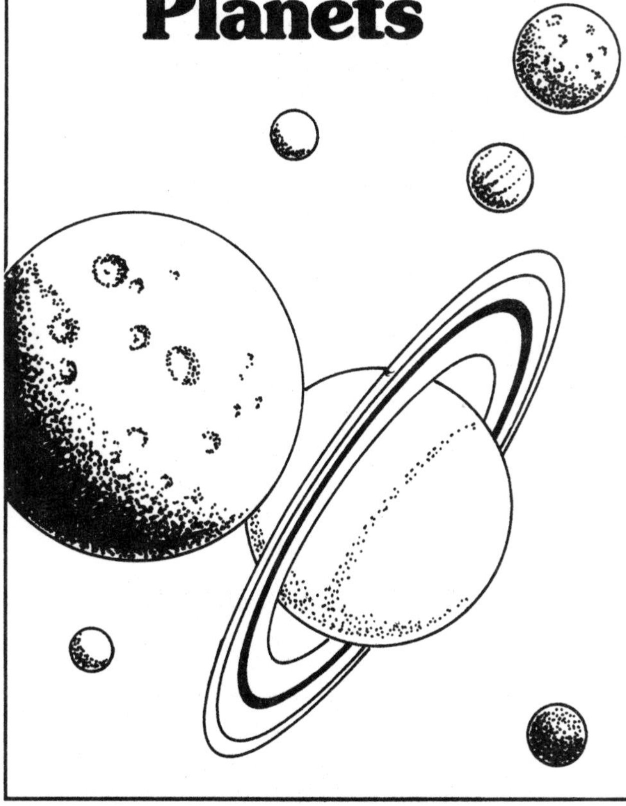

Facts and Fun

Make a mobile of the sun and all nine planets. Be sure they are proportionately correct and in the right order.

Choose a planet. Create a creature who might live there. Describe the characteristics that have allowed it to adapt to its planet.

Compare three planets. Make a chart showing their diameter, number of moons, length of year, temperature, rotation period, and distance from the sun.

Story Starters

As my spacecraft neared Mars I could see . . .

I made an important discovery about one of the planets. . . .

While exploring Mercury . . .

Vocabulary

Mars Earth

Jupiter Uranus

Pluto Venus

Mercury Saturn Neptune

solar system galaxy

sun

atmosphere gravity

revolve

gases

temperature

craters

rings orbit

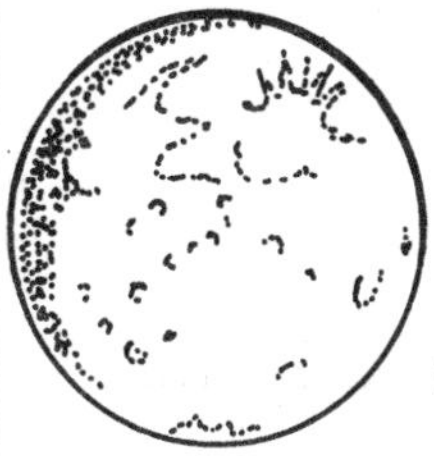

Story Starters

The horse they gave me to ride was a bucking bronco. . . .

I was entrusted with a very important package. . . .

Just as the Indians were closing in behind me . . .

Vocabulary

deliver station

saddlebag

mount

revolver

trail

rider

relay

prairies

horseback

route

mail

dash

Facts and Fun

Read and write a biography about Buffalo Bill, who was one of the pony express riders.

Write a history of mail delivery in the U.S. Include the story of the pony express.

Map out the route of the pony express. Explain how you might have run it and what you would have used to carry the mail.

Pony Express

Story Starters

I had never before seen such huge, colorful flowers! . . .

As I was swinging through the jungle, I passed a village of tree houses! . . .

While walking through the strangely quiet rain forest, I felt hundreds of eyes watching me. . . .

Vocabulary

tropical
equator
Amazon River
transpiration
jungle
moisture humid
Africa
Asia
epiphytes
canopy
emergent layer
crown
Central and South America

Facts and Fun

Why is it important to save the rain forests? What can you do to help?

Describe the three layers of the rain forest and give the characteristics of each.

On a map, locate the rain forests of the world. For each, draw an animal found in that rain forest and write its name next to it.

Reptiles

Facts and Fun

Create a Reptile Study Guide in which you name, describe and illustrate various reptiles. Tell where each reptile lives.

Reptiles can be divided into four main groups. Write about the characteristics of each group.

Make clay models of several dinosaurs. Then create an environment similar to one they most likely lived in, using a large box top, construction paper, and other materials.

Story Starters

The army of reptiles began invading from the land and sea. . . .

My pet chameleon helped me solve the case of the missing homework. . . .

The sea tortoise rescued . . .

Vocabulary

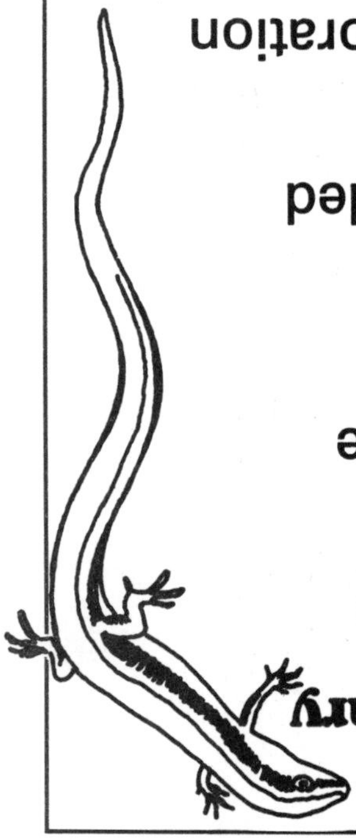

tortoise
scales
crocodile
snake
lizard
cold-blooded
turtle
protective coloration
dinosaur
molt lungs
alligator

Facts and Fun

Make a list of the uses of rocks. Challenge a friend to see if he/she can match your list.

Name four famous statues or buildings made of rock. Tell the kind of rock from which each one is made.

Look up a famous sculptor, such as Michelangelo or Rodin. Write about his/her life. Use clay to imitate one of this person's sculptures.

Rocks

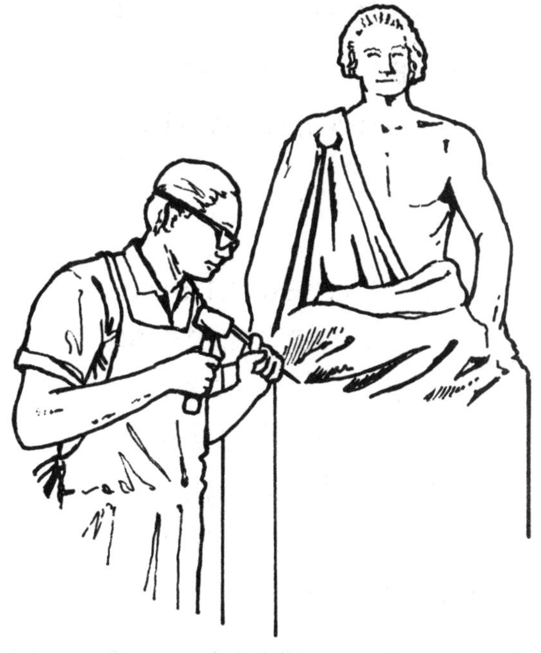

Story Starters

I had always been a rock hound. My latest rock hunting adventure took me to . . .

The granite statue began to move. . . .

While hiking in the woods we came upon a very unusual rock. . . .

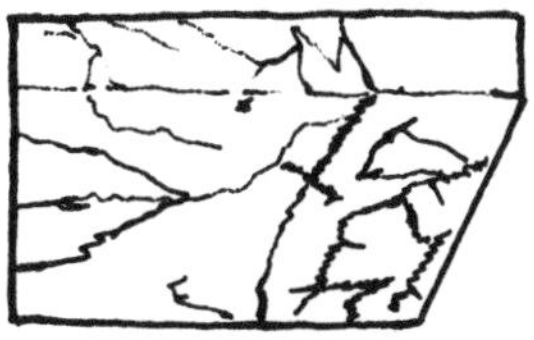

Vocabulary

igneous crystals
sandstone
coal chalk
geologist
sedimentary
basalt
marble slate
limestone
fossils
metamorphic
lava pumice
granite clay
schist

Rodeo

Facts and Fun

Create a brochure advertising a rodeo coming to your area.

Design an outfit fit for a professional cowboy or cowgirl.

If you could be in a rodeo, what would you want to do? Why?

Vocabulary

saddle
cowgirl cowboy
calf roping
chute
bull riding
team roping
timed events
steer wrestling
bareback bronco riding
steer roping
rough stock
arena
lasso spurs
barrel racing

Story Starters

The horses raced around the barrels. . . .

The cowboy's lasso spun high above his head. . . .

The rodeo clown jumped in front of the bull. . . .

Saddle Horses

Facts and Fun

Study the Eohippus, Mesohippus, and Merychippus. Explain how they are similar to and different from the modern horse.

Read about the Mustang. Tell how they originated in the West and what is happening to them today.

Compare English and Western riding styles. Diagram and label the tack used with each style.

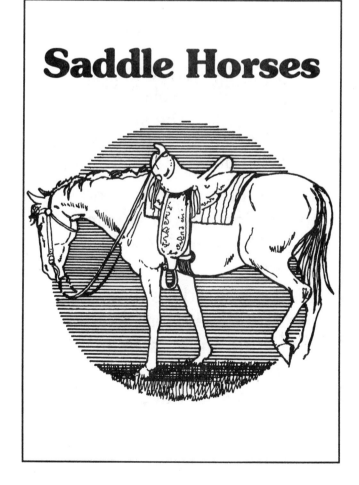

Story Starters

My new horse had been stolen! . . .

I was the horse that Paul Revere rode on his midnight ride. . . .

As the ship sank, I grabbed the mane of the swimming horse and . . .

Vocabulary

hands
star blaze
baldface
Appaloosa
Thoroughbred
Morgan Arabian
American quarter horse
Palomino
paddock stall
American saddlebred
Tennesse walking horse
gait trot canter
tack reins bridle

Story Starters

I was trapped underwater. My air tank was stuck . . .

While diving, I saw a beautiful undersea world. . . .

My air tank was fast becoming empty! . . .

Vocabulary

buoyancy compensator

demand regulator

compressed air

inflate deflate

depth gauges

expeditions

weighted belt

wet suit snorkel

face mask swim fins

bends

air hose

Facts and Fun

Read about Jacques Cousteau and explain why he is important to the sport of scuba diving.

Research the "bends" and other dangerous underwater conditions. Explain each one.

You discovered a sunken ship and have been asked to draw your findings. What treasures were aboard? Why might the ship have sunk?

Scuba Diving

Seashells

Facts and Fun

Mollusks are primarily used for food. Research to name as many as you can. Then make a wordsearch using the names.

Shells are often used to make jewelry and souvenirs. Design something using a variety of shells.

Explain the difference between univalves and bivalves. Give examples of each.

Vocabulary

mollusks
conch
cowrie
clam shell
tooth shell
chiton whelk
mussel snail
scallop nautilus
cone
limpet
oyster
univalve bivalve

Story Starters

I have a wonderful shell collection that . . .

I thought the shell was empty, but when I picked it up . . .

The giant clam was 8 feet wide and 9 feet long! . . .

Skateboarding

Facts and Fun

Make a Skateboarding Dictionary using terms that apply to the sport.

Research the history of skateboarding. When and where did it originate?

Have a Skateboarding Day at school. Design a skateboarders' course.

Vocabulary

maneuvers
rubber-soled shoes
ollie
helmet
push-off
balance kick-turn
fingerflip ramp
knee-elbow pads
wheelie
180's–360's
coffin

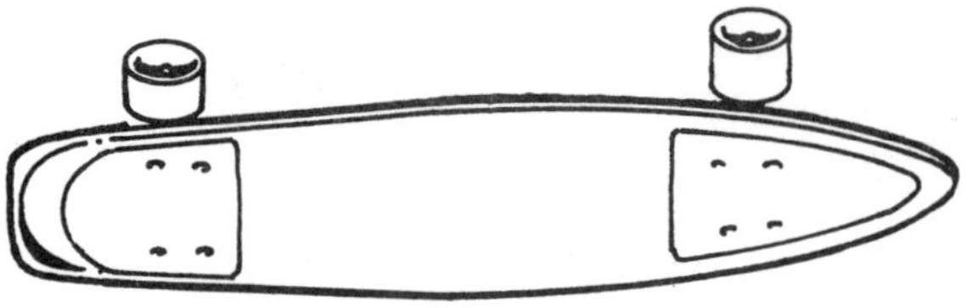

Story Starters

I saw some really hot skateboarding at the park! . . .

I was pretty shaky after I fell, but I got back on my skateboard and . . .

The busy intersection was just up ahead and the skateboarder . . .

Vocabulary

fangs venom
scales
camouflage
vertebrae
reptile
hibernation
slither crawl
forked tongue
molt
boa constrictor king cobra
python garter snake
copperhead rattlesnake
viper prey

Story Starters

Last summer while I was camping, a snake crawled into my backpack. . . .

When I took my pet snake to school . . .

A snake was slithering toward me on the path. . . .

Facts and Fun

Write a paragraph describing how a snake swallows its prey.

Snakes move in four different ways. Research to explain each one.

Look in the dictionary. Find as many words as you can that begin with the word snake and give the definition of each.

Snakes

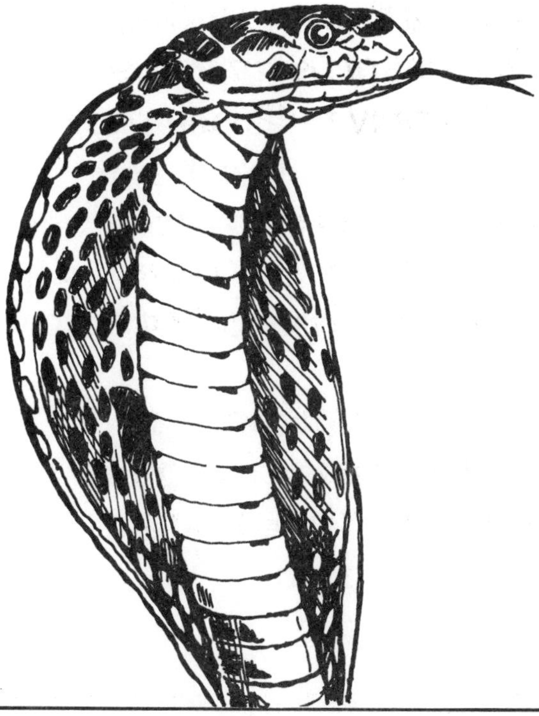

Soccer

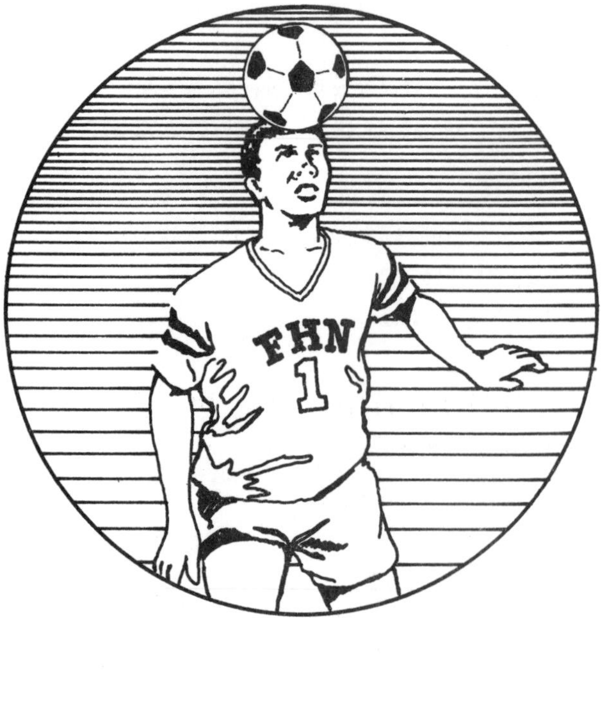

Facts and Fun

Research and write about the World Cup including where and when it has been held, what teams played, and other vital information.

Give a brief history of soccer.

Write an argument to convince someone to play soccer instead of another popular sport.

Story Starters

The last thing I remember is heading the ball. . . .

My magic soccer shoes made me a hero once again. . . .

The game was tied 2 to 2 at halftime. . . .

Vocabulary

defenders sweeper
heading
touch lines goal
midfielders
referee
throw-in free kick
passing tackling
goalkeeper
forwards
trapping dribbling
corner kick
penalty kick
penalty area
goal kick
offside

Softball

Facts and Fun

Make a Venn diagram comparing softball and baseball.

Draw a softball field and list all the positions.

Explain how softball began.

Story Starters

The umpire made another ridiculous call! What was going on? . . .

Judy hit the ball so hard that . . .

Just as the center fielder began to back up . . .

Vocabulary

bunt strike
inning delivery
umpire
single double triple
knuckle ball
squeeze play
force-out
slide foul
slow pitch fast pitch
walk out safe
batter pitcher
catcher fielders
infield outfield

Southwest Native Americans

Facts and Fun

On a map of the United States, identify the area where Southwest Indians lived. Name the tribes that lived in that area and write about their culture.

Research and then construct a model of a Southwest Indian village.

Write a poem about one of the Southwest tribes.

Story Starters

After becoming lost in an ancient Anasazi cliff house, . . .

The Navajos taught me . . .

I am a Pueblo Indian. Today . . .

Vocabulary

ancestors
customs
Kachina dolls
mesas pottery
grinding stones
hogan adobe
sand painting
baskets weavings
moccasins
Apache Navajo Pueblo
fished hunted farmed

Stamp Collecting

Facts and Fun

Design a stamp commemorating a favorite person in your life. Then explain why you chose that person.

Where were stamps first used? Why?

Begin a stamp collection. See how many stamps you can collect in two weeks. Use your relatives, neighbors, and friends as sources.

Story Starters

My sister used my stamp collection to wallpaper her dollhouse! . . .

While I examined a stamp of President Lincoln, the stamp began talking. It told me where a chest of gold had been buried during the Civil War! . . .

He was shocked to find out that the stamp he bought for a nickel at a garage sale was worth $20,000! . . .

Vocabulary

philatelists
watermark
packet duplicate
album tongs
cancellation
imperforate
ink printing
texture
dealer
assortment
stamp hinges
condition valuable
commemorative
magnifying glass

Storms

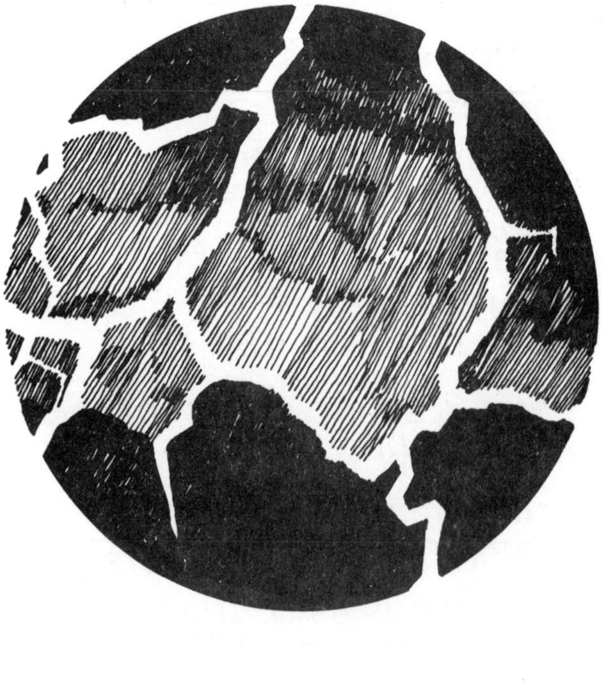

Facts and Fun

Contrast and compare various storms by making a table of their characteristics.

Select three types of storms and tell how you would prepare for each.

Explain what a hurricane is. Make a list of names, dates, and locations of at least five hurricanes.

Story Starters

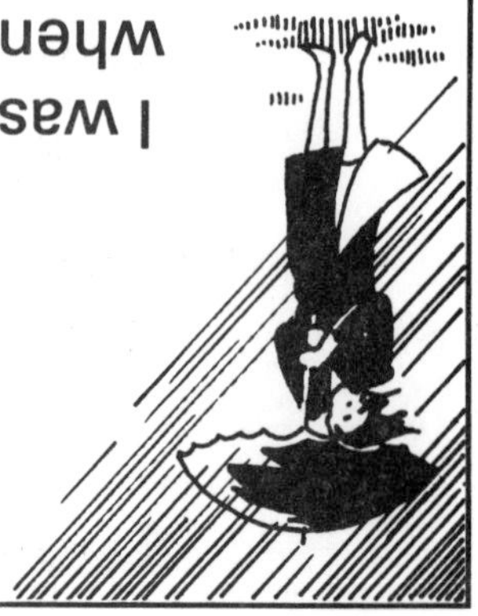

I was babysitting when the tornado siren blasted . . .

After a devastating storm, I led the rescue team . . .

The family was in the elevator when the power went out . . .

Vocabulary

thunderstorm

blizzard typhoon

violent

air pressure

anemometer

wind rain snow ice

sandstorm cyclone

hurricane

tornado

barometer

precipitation predict

humidity

dust storm

Summer Camp

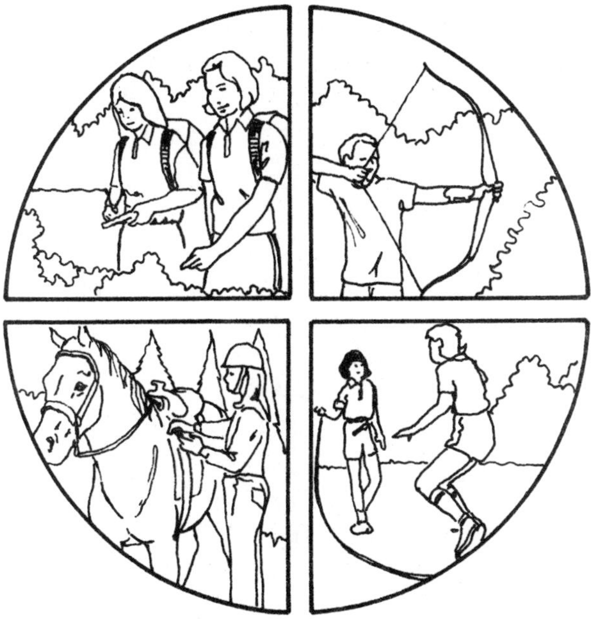

Facts and Fun

Design a camp brochure for the ideal summer camp. Include descriptions, pictures, and maps.

Compile a list of camps you and/or your friends have attended. Next to each camp name, write a favorite experience. Then use this information to make a Camp Directory, listed alphabetically.

Write a new camp song.

Story Starters

When he climbed into his sleeping bag . . .

When our cabin was trashed, we plotted our revenge! . . .

We nicknamed our counselor . . .

Vocabulary

nature
supervision
archery hiking
bugle
calisthenics
counselors
homesick pranks
taps
explore
bunkhouse
canoeing
sleeping bag
swimming
crafts

Story Starters

As I bounced on the board, I realized something was wrong. . . .

As I glanced in the next lane, my competitor was . . .

We were on our way to the championship meet. . . .

Vocabulary

flip turn
official starter
lane
forward back
inward reverse twist
touch pad
approach
false start
straight pike tuck
backstroke freestyle
relay
breaststroke butterfly
degree of difficulty
springboard platform

Facts and Fun

Who holds the women's 400-meter freestyle world record? What was her time and where was she from? Does she hold any other world records?

Invent a new dive or swim stroke. Illustrate it and explain how to do it.

Design a battery-powered swimsuit. Write an advertisement for it.

Swimming & Diving

Track & Field

Facts and Fun

With your teacher organize a Track and Field Day. Prepare a program for the event. List and write a description of each event.

Write an article comparing the ancient Olympic Games with modern Olympic Games.

Have someone time you and some friends in several races. Make a chart showing the times.

Story Starters

I was in first place in the 100-yard dash. Just as I crossed the finish line, . . .

Just as the starting gun sounded, I realized my shoes were . . .

On the bus to the meet . . .

Vocabulary

hurdles
shot-put
pole vault
long jump
high jump
sprints relays
triple jump
running
discus
javelin
hammer throw
decathlon
heptathlon

Story Starters

The spacecraft landed in my yard. . . .

Everybody liked the kid with the green ears. . . .

The extraterrestrial had powers to . . .

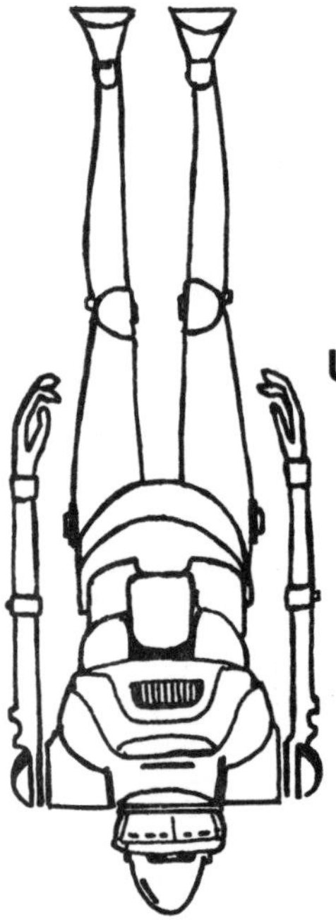

Vocabulary

sighting
alien
intelligent life
civilizations
communication
galaxies
spacecraft
science fiction
flying saucer
Unidentified Flying Objects
United States Air Force
zoom flashes noises

Facts and Fun

Write a newspaper article that describes the sighting and landing of a UFO and the meeting of humans with beings from outer space.

Design a new world and tell where it is located in the universe. Create beings for this world and describe the creatures and their habitats.

Pretend you were an ambassador of the earth and were in charge of showing a visiting space creature around the world. Write about the things you would show it and tell why.

UFOs

The U.S.A.

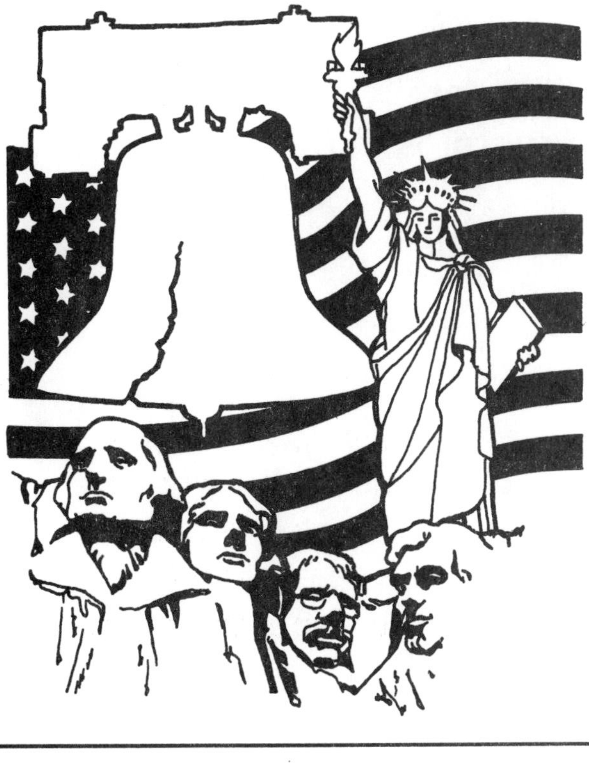

Facts and Fun

What is the Constitution and why is it important to the people of the United States?

Write a conversation you might have had with Betsy Ross concerning the flag.

Draw a diagram of one of the floors of the White House. Label the rooms and tell why each is important.

Story Starters

The time wizard could transport me to any point in American history I chose. . . .

If I could live anywhere in the United States, I would choose . . .

When I opened the invitation from the White House . . .

The ghost that haunts the White House has many stories to tell. . . .

Vocabulary

Stars and Stripes
Statue of Liberty
Lincoln Memorial
Washington Monument
Uncle Sam
The White House
Washington, D.C.
Liberty Bell
bald eagle
Mount Rushmore
Jefferson Memorial
The Constitution
The Star-Spangled Banner

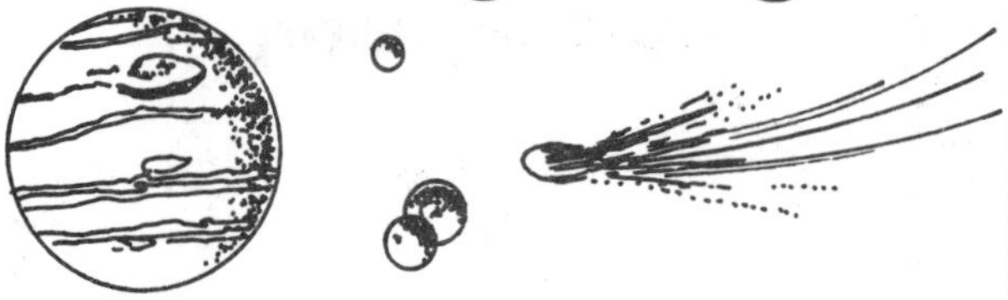

Story Starters

I was aboard the spacecraft sent to destroy the comet headed for Jupiter. . . .

I was drawn through my telescope to the new planet I had just discovered. . . .

Night after night a strange light in the galaxy came a little closer. . . .

Vocabulary

eclipse
asteroid
satellite
position
cosmos
galaxy
telescope
rotation
stars
Milky Way
sun planets
solar system
quasars
astronomer
moon

Facts and Fun

Compare NASA to space programs in other countries.

Describe what an astrologer does.

Choose a space probe such as *Voyager I*, and tell about its discoveries.

The Universe

Facts and Fun

Vultures are considered scavengers. What other types of birds are known as scavengers? Why are scavengers important?

Make a table comparing the wingspans and weights of several different vultures.

The California condor is an endangered bird. Give a short report on it. Include what is being done to protect it.

Vultures

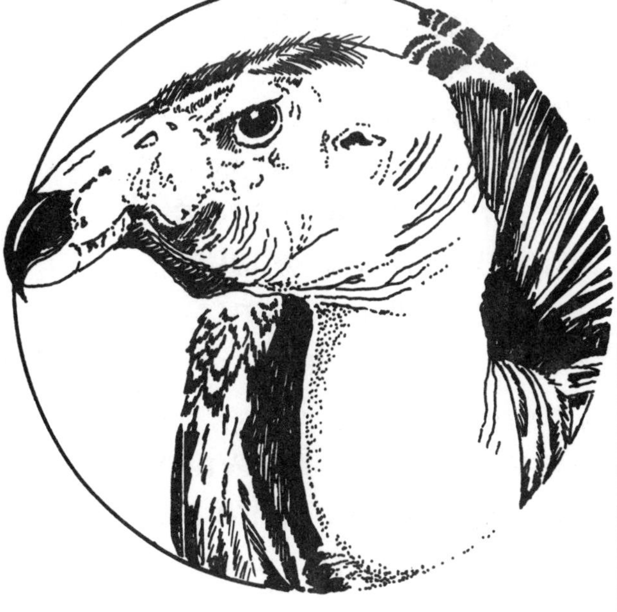

Story Starters

When we saw the soaring vultures we knew . . .

We were lost and had just eaten our last meal when we saw the vultures circling overhead . . .

I trained my pet vulture to . . .

Vocabulary

scavenger
carcass
carrion
bird of prey
nostril hole
talons beak
soar
condor
bald

Story Starters

My friends and I were riding our bikes about a mile from home when it began to rain. . . .

A secret message appeared on the frost-covered lawn. . . .

The blizzard forced us to . . .

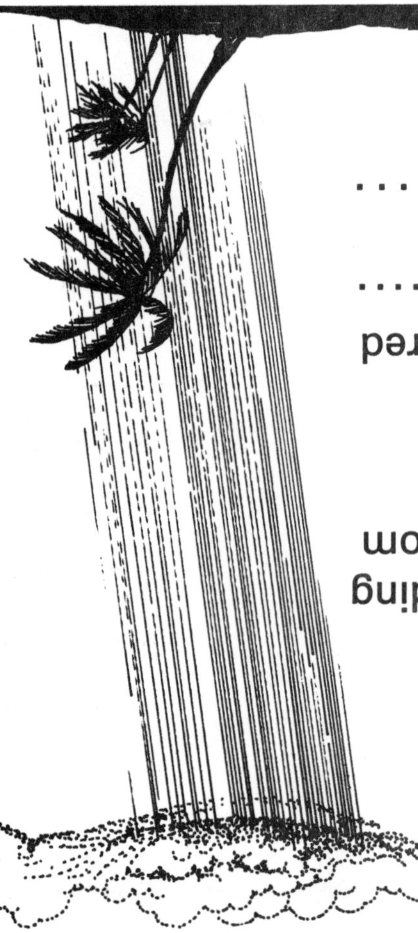

Vocabulary

droplets
rain pour
clouds
dew
wind
frost sleet
air mass
moisture
snow hail
front
evaporation
temperature

Facts and Fun

Explain how a rainbow is formed.

Research to find the rainfall amounts for the various regions of the country. Graph your findings.

Read about or interview a meteorologist. Write about this profession.

Weather

Story Starters

As I led the group deep into the African jungle, we saw a huge cat. . . .

The kitten Ellen bought from the pet store grew into a . . .

One day as I was training the big circus cats . . .

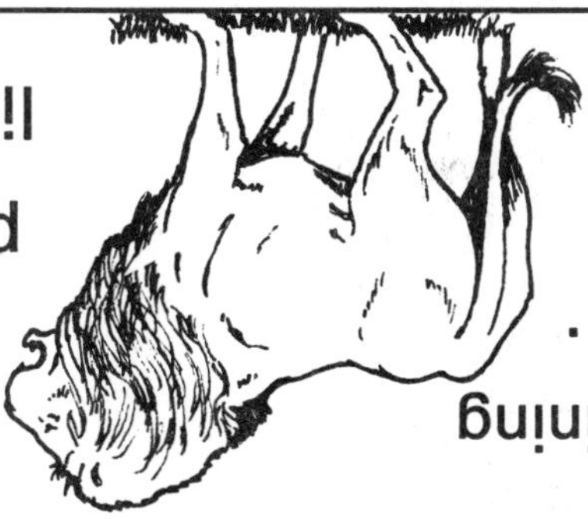

Vocabulary

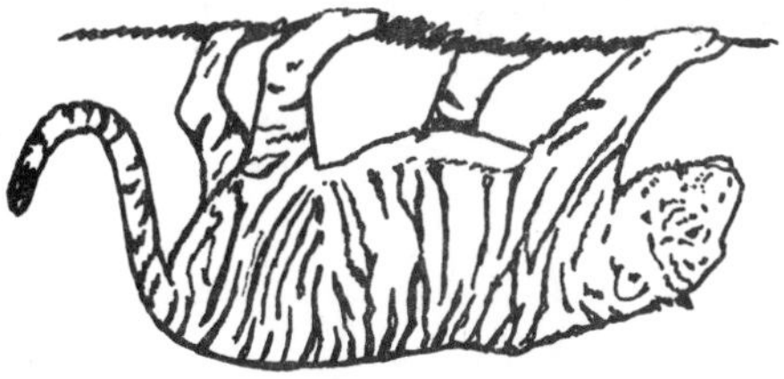

lynx cheetah

carnivore

ferocious

stalk pounce

leopard jaguar

poacher predator

lion cougar tiger

Facts and Fun

Describe the characteristics that all "cats" share.

Read about Joy Adamson and Elsa, the lioness. Write about Adamson's important contributions to our understanding of lions.

Use a map of the world to chart the areas where wild cats live.

Wild Cats

Wild West

Facts and Fun

Read about the Gold Rush. Explain how it influenced the development of the West.

Make a wanted poster for a notorious wild West outlaw. Write the outlaw's biography on the back of the poster.

Design a home that a family of settlers might have lived in. Explain why its features would have been appropriate.

Vocabulary

prairie
gold rush
canteen
longhorn cattle
wagon train
Indians
chaps spurs bandanna
ranchers
settlers
outlaws
stagecoach
frontier
prospector claims
homesteaders
cowboy hat

Story Starters

The herd of longhorns was stampeding toward the wagon train. . . .

My usual day as a cowboy began . . .

The land my family had purchased didn't fit the description we had been given at all. . . .

Facts and Fun

Explain the different weight classes for high school and college wrestling. Why is weight important in this sport?

Describe the scoring system for a wrestling match.

A wrestler wears a singlet and headgear. Design a wrestling uniform for your school.

Wrestling

Story Starters

I was caught in a headlock when . . .

I was going for the pin . . .

The new headgear gave me special powers. . . .

Vocabulary

ride
opponent
singlet
referee's position
pin fall headlock
pickup holds
strength
take down
near fall
balance coordination
maneuvers
switch
speed
escape

Your Five Senses

Facts and Fun

How is your eye like a camera? Explain how it works.

Name the specialists who help keep our senses working properly.

Write about someone you know or have read about who is blind or deaf.

Story Starters

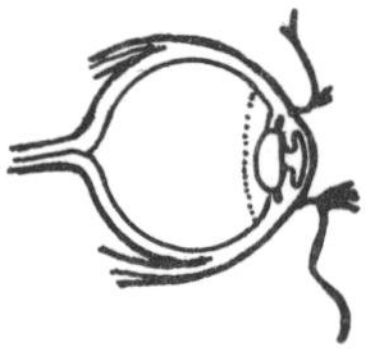

The most fantastic sight in all the world . . .

The smells didn't fit the foods. . . .

The sound of the ________ made me . . .

Vocabulary

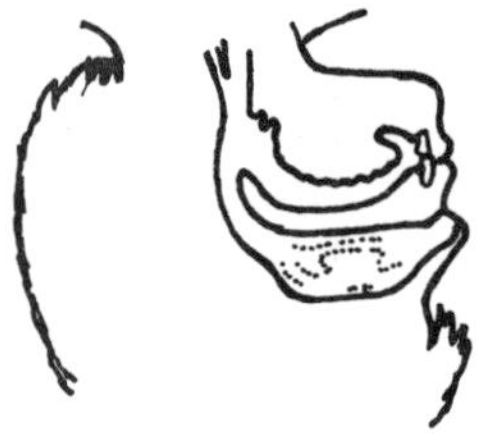

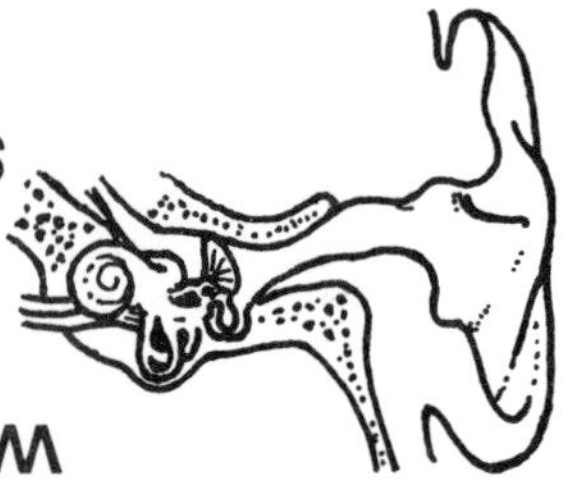

feel skin

taste tongue

hear ear

sight eye

smell nose

pain hot cold

sweet salty sour

whispers shout

blurry clear

stinky fragrant